ACTIVE
FOR
LIFE

JUNIOR CYCLE PE

FERGAL LYONS   SARAHJANE BELTON   NICOLA CREAN   IVAN O'MAHONY

Contents

Introduction — iii

Strand 1 (Physical activity for health and wellbeing)

1 **Fundamental movement skills** — 2

2 **Health-related activity** — 30

Strand 2 (Games)

3 **Games** — 58

Strand 3 (Individual and team challenges)

4 **Athletics** — 138

5 **Aquatics** — 168

6 **Adventure activities** — 186

Strand 4 (Dance and Gymnastics)

7 **Dance** — 216

8 **Gymnastics** — 246

Reflecting on my wellbeing

9 **Apps for wellbeing** — 280

Reflective Journal — 284

Introduction

Active for Life provides you with the opportunity to record in one handy location all your learning in PE class over your three years of Junior Cycle. With a variety of assessment tools covering every area of the PE curriculum, you will be challenged in many ways. Whether it is analysing a video clip of your running technique or reflecting on the role you played in a gymnastics presentation, you are at the centre of the learning experience throughout this workbook. There are many occasions to reflect on how you feel and what you have learned along the way. This is important because PE is not just a class you take part in once a week – it provides you with the skills and knowledge necessary to be physically active and healthy for the rest of your life.

My PE Contract

The five most important expectations and rules of our PE class are:

1. _____

   _____

2. _____

   _____

3. _____

   _____

4. _____

   _____

5. _____

   _____

Failing to meet these expectations will result in:

_____

_____

Attending PE class without PE gear (without a valid reason) will result in:

_____

_____

Student signature   Parent signature   Teacher signature

_____   _____   _____

The Key Skills of Junior Cycle

Your Junior Cycle experience is governed by eight Key Skills. These Key Skills are important tools that will help you live a long, happy and healthy life. The following pages will explain how these Key Skills are used in this workbook and how they can contribute to your overall wellbeing.

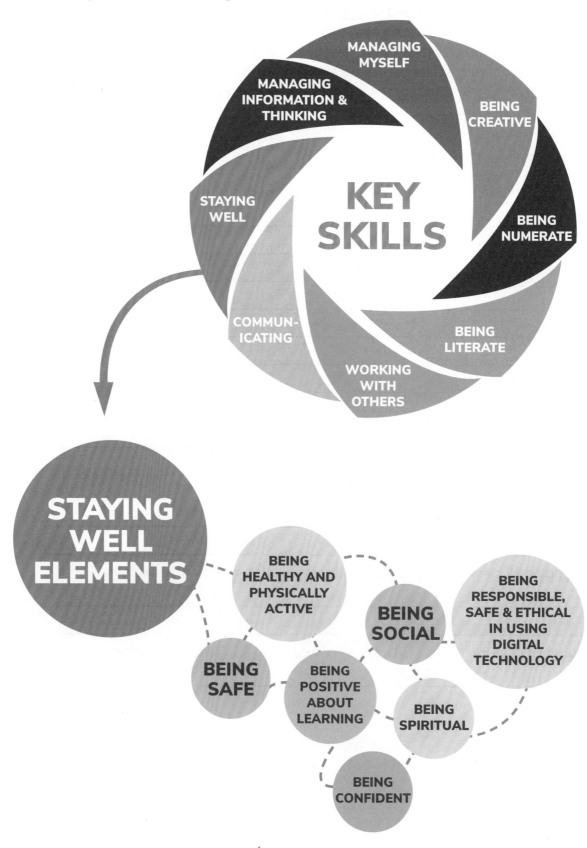

The eight Key Skills

Managing myself
- Understanding yourself and how your body works
- Designing personal improvement plans
- Using digital technology to manage yourself and your learning
- Setting and achieving personal goals through the development of new skills
- Reflecting on your own and a partner's performance

Managing information and thinking
- Providing accurate, helpful feedback to teammates
- Gathering, recording and evaluating data through questionnaires and research projects
- Thinking critically and reflecting on data gathered to make judgements

Working with others
- Participating successfully in team events
- Learning to respect differences and utilise each other's strengths
- Developing relationships skills, cooperating and respecting differences through partner work and group work
- Cooperating with others and learning by giving and receiving constructive feedback

Being creative
- Learning creatively
- Implementing ideas from personal improvement plans
- Using new skills and abilities to design and perform sequences of movement

Communicating
- Using appropriate language to provide feedback
- Contributing effectively as part of a team
- Cooperating with classmates to achieve mutual goals
- Expressing themes through movement

Being literate
- Expressing ideas clearly and accurately
- Reading with critical understanding, interpreting maps and symbols used

Being numerate
- Using mathematical approaches to solving PE-related problems
- Counting beats and identifying patterns of movement

Staying well

Being healthy and physically active

- You will learn about your body, nutrition and how much physical activity you need to do every day to be healthy.

- You will learn that there are many different ways to be active: on your own, with friends, in large groups, etc.

- You will understand the effect physical activity has on your body, and how to judge whether you are being active enough for your health and wellbeing.

- You will get to experience how different types of sports and activities can help you to feel better, both physically and emotionally.

Being safe and responsible

- You will learn how to safely and correctly handle potentially dangerous equipment and interact with others in different settings, such as a playing field or swimming pool.

- You will learn how to move safely and how to support others to do the same.

- Using technology in a safe, ethical and responsible way plays a huge role in this workbook.

- You will be challenged to improve your own movement technique, fitness and ability, and will also be responsible for developing personal improvement plans in many areas.

Being positive about learning, and being social

- You will learn to be positive and constructive when sharing feedback with others.

- You will learn that there are lots of types of activities that you are already really good at, and how you can go about getting even better.

- You will learn to work with a partner and in small groups to help each other complete tasks, and to improve all your abilities.

- You will learn to be confident in your physical body, and in your abilities to keep yourself healthy and active for life.

Being confident and spiritual

- Physical activity and sport have something for everyone and they teach you how to move with confidence.

- Many of the activities in this workbook are individual and give you the chance to focus on personal development.

- Gymnastics teaches you how to move with control, etc., which in turn helps you to move with confidence.

- In dance and gymnastics you will learn about aesthetics and how to appreciate the beauty in movements.

Key to icons in this student learning record

Wellbeing icons

With *wellbeing* now a major focus of the Junior Cycle programme, PE has been identified as an important area to develop your physical, psychological and social wellbeing. Of the six key indicators listed below, almost all can be experienced and developed in PE class on a daily basis. These indicators appear throughout this workbook. When you see them, pause to reflect on how you feel in that moment and how the activity you are partaking in can impact on how you feel.

INDICATORS OF WELLBEING

ACTIVE
- Am I a confident and skilled participant in physical activity?
- How physically active am I?

CONNECTED
- Do I feel connected to my school, my friends, my community and the wider world?
- Do I appreciate that my actions and interactions impact on my own wellbeing and that of others, in local and global contexts?

RESPONSIBLE
- Do I take action to protect and promote my wellbeing and that of others?
- Do I make healthy eating choices?
- Do I know where my safety is at risk and do I make right choices?

RESILIENT
- Do I believe that I have the coping skills to deal with life's challenges?
- Do I know where I can go for help?
- Do I believe that with effort I can achieve?

RESPECTED
- Do I feel that I am listened to and valued?
- Do I have positive relationships with my friends, my peers and my teachers?
- Do I show care and respect for others?

AWARE
- Am I aware of my thoughts, feelings and behaviours and can I make sense of them?
- Am I aware of what my personal values are and do I think through my decisions?
- Do I understand what helps me to learn and how I can improve?

Traffic light icons

When you see traffic lights at the top of a table, choose **one** of the colours to tick:

 Mastered

 Nearly there

 Needs more practice

Additional icons

 Partner work

 Self-check

 Video recording

 FMS signpost

Fundamental movement skills

Chapter 01

Introduction

Fundamental movement skills (FMS) are the basic building blocks of movement. They play a huge role, not only in sport, but also in our everyday lives. If you can master a number of basic FMS, then you will be able to perform more sport-specific movements in a wide range of sporting and non-sporting situations.

Mastering these base movements will provide you with the tools to participate successfully in many sports and activities. For example: after learning the basic FMS of kicking, you can then apply it to different kicking techniques in football, rugby or Australian Rules football. It's kind of like reading: if we knew only a certain number of words, and never really learned to read new words, we would only ever be able to read a very small number of books. But by mastering the building blocks of reading – our sounds and the basic rules of English – suddenly, we open up a whole library of books we can choose from. FMS are the same: once we master these basic movements, we can take these skills and adapt them to any physical activity or sport that we might want to do. That's our whole library of movement!

These skills are not sport-specific so may be different from some of the techniques you have learned in the past. Remember that FMS are the base line movements that are then built upon in various ways in specific sports and recreational activities.

Common terms

Fundamental movement skills (FMS)	The basic patterns of movement that open the door to a wide range of physical activities
Sport-specific movement skills	Fundamental movement skills that have been adapted to suit a specific sport or physical activity
Locomotor skills	Skills for moving your body from one place to another in different ways: • Running • Dodging • Jumping for height • Jumping for distance
Stability skills	Balancing the body when still, and stabilising the body during movement: • Landing
Manipulative skills	Engaging with an outside object using various body parts: • Kicking • Throwing • Catching • Two-handed strike
Improvement plan	A plan you design to practise, monitor and develop FMS over time
Technical point	A technical point of a skill is one aspect of correct technique. Most FMS have 6–8 technical points to master.

Assessment tools

1. Running

Running is a vital FMS. It is a gateway skill to many sports and physical activities. When you improve your running technique, you can run faster and more efficiently.

To assess your partner's technique:

- Ask your partner to run as fast as they can in a straight line for at least 20 m.

- Watch your partner from the side and from the front, to get a full view of their technique.

- Watch your partner at least once for each technical point. For running, watch your partner run 20 m at least seven times.

Choose a partner to work with

1. Ask your partner to assess your technique and to tick 'Mastered', 'Nearly there' or 'Needs more practice'.
2. Then work with your partner to answer the questions on p.5.

Correct technique	What it looks like	Mastered	Nearly there	Needs more practice
Is the head up and stable? Are the eyes looking forward?				
Are the elbows bent at 90 degrees (L shape) throughout the run?				
Do the arms drive forwards and backwards in opposition to the legs (left leg and right arm; right leg and left arm)?				
Is there a high knee-lift, with the thigh almost parallel to the ground?				

Is the kickback close to the buttocks (at least 90 degrees)				
Running at full speed, does the foot contact the ground predominantly with the ball of the foot (not flat-footed and not with the heel)?				
Does the runner lean slightly forward when accelerating, and slightly backwards when slowing down?				

What I did well:

_____

_____

_____

How I can improve:

_____

_____

_____

My plan for improving:

_____

_____

_____

List three settings where running technique is important.

1. _____

2. _____

3. _____

2. Catching

Catching is an important part of many sports, such as Gaelic football, rounders, rugby, basketball and Ultimate Frisbee. When you master the basic catch, you can use this technique to excel in a range of sports and activities.

To assess your technique:

- Record yourself or ask a friend to record you.
- Take several recordings: some from the side, and some from the front (diagonally).
- Throw a tennis ball at a wall and catch it again from a distance of 5 m for 30 seconds.
- Catch with two hands, if possible.
- Watch at least one recording for each technical point.

Self-check

1. Fill in the table below to assess your technique. Tick 'I've mastered it', 'I'm nearly there' or 'I need more practice'. Be honest and be strict!
2. Then answer the questions on p.7.

Correct technique	What it looks like	I've mastered it	I'm nearly there	I need more practice
Are your eyes focused on the ball throughout the catch?				
Do your feet move to place your body in the path of ball?				
Are your fingers relaxed and slightly cupped to receive the ball?				
Do your hands reach out to meet the object?				

Do your elbows bend at least 90 degrees to absorb the impact of the catch?

Do you use your hands (not your chest or tummy) to catch and control the ball?

What I did well:

_____

_____

_____

How I can improve:

_____

_____

_____

My plan for improving:

_____

_____

_____

3. Dodging

When you learn the technique of dodging, you can change direction quickly to evade an opponent in a wide range of game settings.
You can avoid tackles in rugby, run away from a catcher in tag, and make your way through an obstacle course. Good technique in dodging will help you in many sports.

To assess your partner's technique:

- Ask your partner to run repeatedly through a slalom of cones, dodging at each turn.

- Watch your partner from the side and from the front, to get a full view of their technique.

- Watch your partner at least once for each technical point. For dodging, watch your partner dodge through the slalom at least five times.

Choose a partner to work with

1. Ask your partner to assess your technique and to tick 'Mastered', 'Nearly there' or 'Needs more practice'.
2. Then work with your partner to answer the questions on p.9.

Correct technique	What it looks like	Mastered	Nearly there	Needs more practice
Is the head up? Are the eyes mainly focused forward (not always looking at the ground)?				
When changing direction, is power generated by planting and pushing off from the outside leg (right leg when dodging left)?				
During the dodge, is the knee bent? Is the push-off made from the outside of the foot?				

Can the dodge be performed equally on the left side and on the right side?

Is there a deceptive element to the dodge (e.g. leaning one way and going the other, looking one way and going the other)?

What I did well:

_____

_____

_____

How I can improve:

_____

_____

_____

My plan for improving:

_____

_____

_____

When dodging, muscular strength is used to generate force in the quad muscle to change direction. What does this mean?

_____

_____

_____

_____

_____

_____

_____

_____

_____

_____

_____

4. Throwing

It is important to master the FMS of throwing. It provides the basic movement pattern for sport-specific throwing actions in games such as rounders, basketball and dodgeball, and throwing the javelin in athletics.

To assess your technique:

- Record yourself or ask a friend to record you.

- Take several recordings: some from the side, and some from the front (diagonally).

- Throw a tennis ball as hard as you can, either to a partner standing at least 10 m away, or at a wall.

- Throw with one hand.

- Watch at least one recording for each technical point.

Self-check

1. Fill in the table below to assess your technique. Tick 'I've mastered it', 'I'm nearly there' or 'I need more practice'. Be honest and be strict!

2. Then answer the questions on page p.11.

Correct technique	What it looks like	I've mastered it	I'm nearly there	I need more practice
Are your eyes focused on the target (where the throw is going) throughout?				
Are you standing side-on with your non-throwing shoulder towards the target?				
In preparing to throw, do you bring your throwing arm back behind your body and swing it down and backwards?				

Do you step towards the target with the foot of your non-throwing side? Do you transfer weight from the back foot to the front foot?

Do your hips, and then your shoulders, rotate forwards during the throwing action?

Does your throwing arm stay close to your ear as it moves forwards?

After releasing the ball, does your arm follow through in the direction of the target and then down across the body?

Note: Sometimes it helps to raise the non-throwing arm and point it in the direction of the target during the preparation phase, and then lower the non-throwing arm when throwing. Give it a go!

What I did well:

_____

_____

_____

How I can improve:

_____

_____

_____

My plan for improving:

_____

_____

_____

5. Landing

For safety reasons, landing is a vital skill to learn. When you learn to land with correct technique, you will reduce your chances of impact injuries. Good landing technique can improve your performance in many different activities.

To assess your partner's technique:

- Ask your partner to stand on a low bench and to jump off using both feet, and landing on both feet.

- Watch your partner from the side and from the front, to get a full view of their technique.

- Watch your partner at least once for each technical point. For landing, watch your partner at least seven times.

Choose a partner to work with

1. Ask your partner to assess your technique and to tick 'Mastered', 'Nearly there' or 'Needs more practice'.

2. Then work with your partner to answer the questions on p.13.

Correct technique	What it looks like	Mastered	Nearly there	Needs more practice
Is the head up and stable? Are the eyes looking straight ahead?				
On landing, are the arms stretched out in front to maintain balance?				
Do the knees bend?				
Do the buttocks tuck under the body in a squat-like position?				

Do the feet land wide apart in a stable position (at least shoulder-width apart)?				
On impact, do the feet contact the ground in the quick order of toe-ball-heel (not flat-footed)?				
Is the landing position held for at least two seconds?				

What I did well:

_____

_____

How I can improve:

_____

_____

My plan for improving:

_____

_____

Why is it important to be able to land safely?
Give reasons and examples.

_____

_____

_____

_____

_____

_____

_____

_____

_____

_____

_____

6. Kicking

Kicking is a part of many of the most popular sports in Ireland, including Gaelic football, soccer and rugby. Kicking skills can take many forms, depending on the sport, but the FMS of kicking remain the same.

To assess your technique:

- Record yourself or ask a friend to record you.

- Take several recordings: some from the side, and some from the front (diagonally).

- Kick a ball with maximum power, either at a wall or to a partner some distance away. Safety is important: ensure there is nobody in your way.

- Watch at least one recording for each technical point.

Self-check

1. Fill in the table below to assess your technique. Tick 'I've mastered it', 'I'm nearly there' or 'I need more practice'. Be honest and be strict!

2. Then answer the questions on p.15.

Correct technique	What it looks like	I've mastered it	I'm nearly there	I need more practice
Do you approach the ball from behind and slightly from the side?				
Prior to kicking, do you place your non-kicking foot to the side of the ball?				
In preparing to kick, do you swing your kicking leg back to make an angle of at least 90 degrees?				
When kicking, do you make contact with the ball using the shoe laces or instep of your foot?				

During contact, do you swing the arm opposite your kicking leg forward and sideways?				
Do you follow through in the direction of the target?				
Throughout the kicking action, do you keep your eyes focused on the ball?				

What I did well:

_____

_____

How I can improve:

_____

_____

My plan for improving:

_____

_____

_____

7. Jumping for height

The FMS of jumping for height is a measure of how high you can jump straight up into the air off both feet, before landing safely on both feet. The technique can be applied to sport-specific jumps in basketball, volleyball, football, gymnastics and dance. Muscular strength and body control are important for generating power and controlling the movement while in the air.

To assess your partner's technique:

- Ask your partner to stand perpendicular to a wall at a distance of 30 cm. Your partner jumps as high as they can and touches the wall at the highest point, before landing safely.

- Watch your partner from the side and from the front, to get a full view of their technique.

- Watch your partner at least once for each technical point. For jumping for height, watch your partner at least seven times. How high they touch the wall is not important: focus on correct technique only.

Choose a partner to work with

1. Ask your partner to assess your technique and to tick 'Mastered', 'Nearly there' or 'Needs more practice'.
2. Then work with your partner to answer the questions on p.17.

Correct technique	What it looks like	Mastered	Nearly there	Needs more practice
Are the eyes focused forwards or upwards throughout the jump?				
Just before the jump, are the knees bent? Are the arms extended behind the body?				
During the jump, do the legs forcefully straighten in the air?				
Do the arms swing forcefully upwards in time with the legs?				

Do both the arms and legs straighten while in the air?					
On landing, do the hips, knees and ankles bend to absorb the shock?					
To control the landing, does the jumper land on both feet, with no more than one step in any direction?					

What I did well:

_____

_____

_____

How I can improve:

_____

_____

_____

My plan for improving:

_____

_____

_____

A lot of power is generated when jumping for height.
What muscles generate this power?

_____

_____

_____

8. Jumping for distance

Jumping for distance is a key FMS for developing rhythm and coordination between the legs and the arms. The action involves jumping as far as you can, from two feet, and landing on both feet in a controlled manner. This skill is a core part of many sports, including the long jump, diving, dance and gymnastics.

To assess your technique:

- Record yourself or ask a partner to record you.

- Take several recordings: some from the side, and some from the front (diagonally).

- Measure the length of your body: lie on the ground and place one cone at your head and one cone at your feet. The target is to jump the length of your body (or as much of that length as possible) while keeping control of your landing.

- Watch at least one recording for each technical point.

Self-check

1. Fill in the table below to assess your technique. Tick 'I've mastered it', 'I'm nearly there' or 'I need more practice'. Be honest and be strict!
2. Then answer the questions on p.19.

Correct technique	What it looks like	I've mastered it	I'm nearly there	I need more practice
Are you in the 'ready' position: bending the knees, hips and ankles?				
Is your head up? Are your eyes focused forwards?				
Do you explode forwards from the ready position?				
To generate power, do you swing your arms behind your body, and then swing them quickly forwards and upwards?				

Do you push off from both feet together? Are your toes the last part of the body to leave the ground?				
Do you land on both feet at the same time? Do you bend the hips, knees and ankles to absorb the impact?				
Is your landing controlled and balanced? Are your feet at least shoulder-width apart?				

What I did well:

_____

_____

_____

How I can improve:

_____

_____

_____

My plan for improving:

9. Two-handed strike

The two-handed strike is an important skill in many of the most popular sports in Ireland. When you master the two-handed strike, you can improve at rounders, hurling, tennis and golf. It is worth noting that in each sport, there is a sport-specific strike technique. For example, in golf the strike is in a large circular arc; while in tennis, the strike is in more of a straight line. The FMS of the two-handed strike is a straight striking action similar to that in baseball or rounders. When you master this technique, you can apply it in many different sports.

Work in a group of three:

- Ask one partner to be the thrower. Ask another partner to be the striker. You will assess the striker.

- Ask the thrower to stand 5 m away from the striker, and to lob a ball gently into their path.

- The striker will hit the ball into open space or at a wall.

- Watch the striker from the side and from the front (diagonally), to get a full view of their technique.

- Watch the striker at least once for each technical point. For the two-handed strike, watch the striker at least seven times.

Choose a partner to work with

1. Assess your partner's technique and tick 'Mastered', 'Nearly there' or 'Needs more practice'.
2. Then work with your partner to answer the questions on p.21.

Correct technique	What it looks like	Mastered	Nearly there	Needs more practice
Does the striker stand side-on to the target?				
Are the eyes focused on the ball throughout the striking action?				

Are the hands together at the base of the bat?				
In the preparation phase, are the feet shoulder-width apart? Are the knees slightly bent? Is the weight on the back foot?				
During the striking action, does the striker step forward with the front foot? Does the striker rotate the hips and shoulders?				
At the point of contact with the bat, are the arms extended fully?				
After the bat makes contact with the ball, does the striker follow through, and around the body?				

What I did well:

_____

_____

How I can improve:

_____

_____

My plan for improving:

_____

_____

The two-handed strike is one of the most difficult FMS to master. In your opinion, why is this?

_____

_____

_____

_____

How to complete your assessment

1. **Choose** one FMS to develop over a four-week period.

2. Provide a **rationale** for choosing the skill.

3. **Measure your starting point**. Fill in a self-assessment wheel to identify which technical points of your chosen skill can be improved.

4. Write your **improvement plan**.

5. Keep a **diary** for four weeks.

6. Fill in another self-assessment wheel to **measure your progress** during the plan.

7. **Reflect** on what you have learned.

1. My chosen FMS

2. My rationale

Outline your reasons for choosing this FMS:
- Explain the role of this skill in a sport you play.

_____

_____

_____

_____

- Describe how the skill (or the sport-specific development of the skill) is used.

_____

_____

_____

_____

- Explain why it is important to master the skill and how you may benefit from improving your technique.

_____

_____

_____

_____

3. Measuring my skill: Self-Assessment Wheel 1

Complete Self-Assessment Wheel 1 on p.25 to identify which technical points of the FMS you will focus on.

1. Fill in a short description for each of the technical points of your chosen FMS.
2. Fill in your current skill level for each of the technical points.
3. To assess your current skill level, refer to the correct technique tables on pp.4–21.
4. For each of the technical points, award yourself a score between 1 and 4. For example, a score of 1 means: 'I cannot do this.' If you score 1, shade one segment of the wheel. If you score 2, shade two segments.
5. Then zoom out and look at the entire wheel. It will be clear to see which technical points are mastered, and which can be improved.

Below is an example of a completed self-assessment wheel.

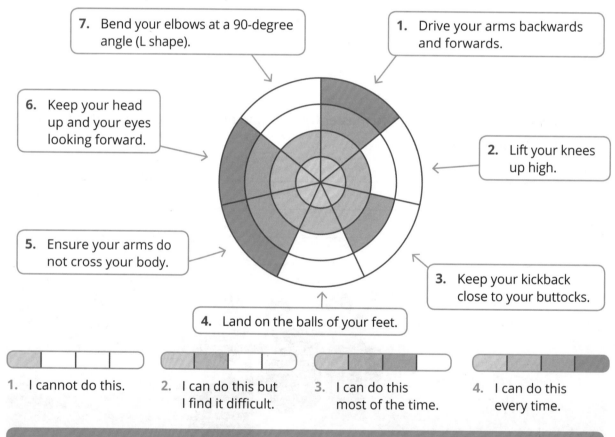

7. Bend your elbows at a 90-degree angle (L shape).

1. Drive your arms backwards and forwards.

6. Keep your head up and your eyes looking forward.

2. Lift your knees up high.

5. Ensure your arms do not cross your body.

3. Keep your kickback close to your buttocks.

4. Land on the balls of your feet.

1. I cannot do this.
2. I can do this but I find it difficult.
3. I can do this most of the time.
4. I can do this every time.

What I am doing well:
- My arms do not cross my body.
- My kickback is close to my buttocks.
- My arms drive backwards and forwards well.
- My head is up and my eyes are looking forward.

What I need to improve on:
- Sometimes I lose the L shape in my arms, especially when I bring my arm back.
- I am not fully landing on the balls of my feet when sprinting. I think my knee lift is not high enough. I think these two things may be related.

Self-Assessment Wheel 1

Skill chosen _____

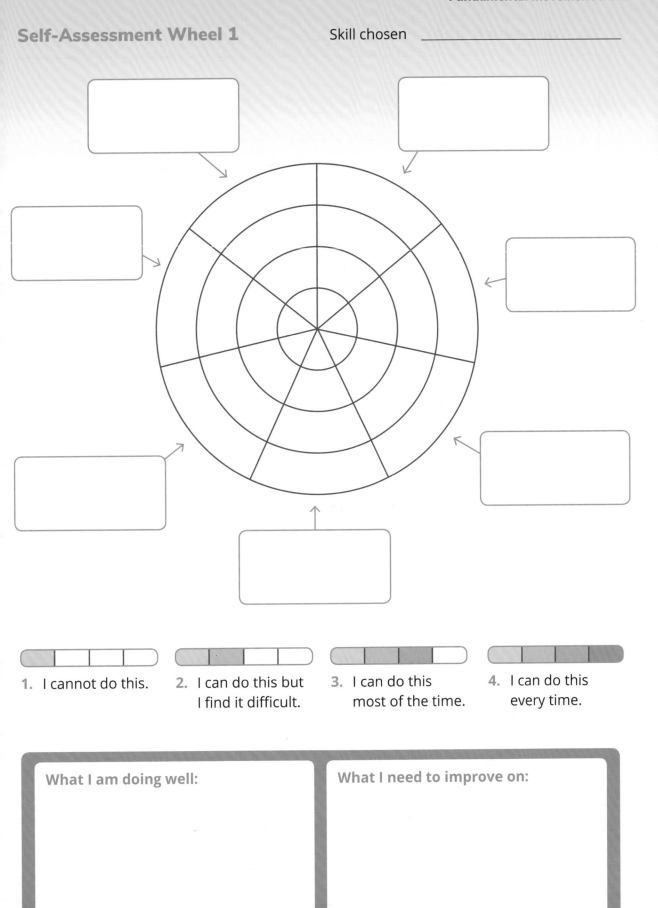

1. I cannot do this.
2. I can do this but I find it difficult.
3. I can do this most of the time.
4. I can do this every time.

What I am doing well:

What I need to improve on:

4. My four-week improvement plan

5. Diary of my improvement plan

Week 1

Week 2

Week 3

Week 4

6. Measuring my progress: Self-Assessment Wheel 2

Self-Assessment Wheel 2   Skill chosen _____

After completing your four-week improvement plan, it is time to check if your skill level has improved. Complete Self-Assessment Wheel 2, as you completed Self-Assessment Wheel 1.

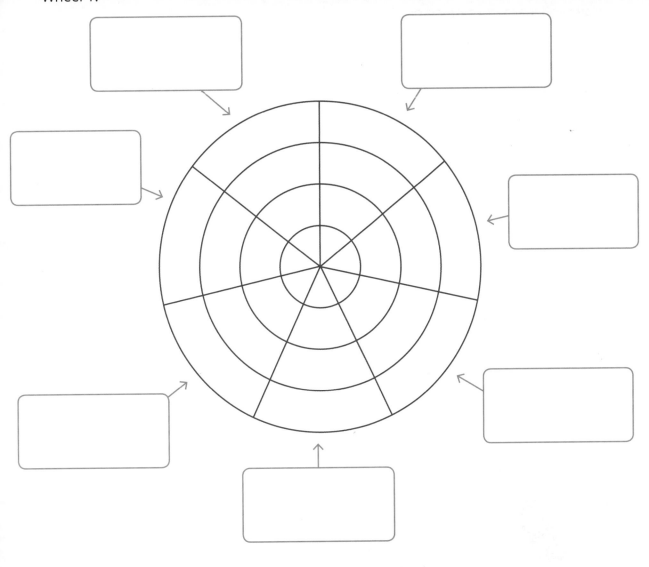

1. I cannot do this.

2. I can do this but I find it difficult.

3. I can do this most of the time.

4. I can do this every time.

What I am doing well:	What I need to improve on:

7. Reflection

Write about what you learned during this process. Reflect on the following points.

- Did your skill level improve or not? Why?

- Will this self-assessment influence your participation in sports? How?

- What part of the process did you find most valuable?

- Have you learned anything new?

Strand review

In this chapter, you learned about:

- Fundamental (FMS), locomotor, stability and manipulative skills ☐
- The difference between FMS and sport-specific movement skills ☐
- Assessing FMS using a table of technical points ☐
- Assessing your own ability to perform a skill, using recordings ☐
- Using technology to record a partner performing a skill ☐

- Assessing a partner's ability to perform a skill, using technical points ☐
- Giving feedback to a partner and discussing correct and incorrect technique ☐
- Developing an improvement plan ☐
- Practising FMS in isolation and then applying them to sports of your choice ☐
- Identifying FMS in various sports and physical activities ☐

Look back over the activities you completed. Tick the skills you used.

Managing Myself	Staying Well	Managing Information and Thinking	Being Numerate
I know myself better ☐	I am healthy and active ☐	I gathered and analysed information ☐	I estimated, predicted and calculated ☐
I made decisions ☐	I am social ☐	I thought creatively ☐	I was interested in problem-solving ☐
I set goals ☐	I am safe ☐	I thought about what I learned ☐	
I achieved goals ☐	I feel confident ☐	I used digital technology to access, manage and share information ☐	
I thought about what I learned ☐	I feel positive about what I learned ☐		
I used technology to learn ☐			

Being Creative	Working with Others	Communicating	Being Literate
I thought about things from a different point of view ☐	I developed relationships ☐	I listened to my classmates ☐	I understood some new words ☐
I put ideas into action ☐	I dealt with conflict ☐	I expressed myself ☐	I wrote for different reasons ☐
I learned in a creative way ☐	I cooperated ☐	I performed/ presented ☐	I expressed my ideas clearly ☐
I was creative with digital technology ☐	I respected difference ☐	I had a discussion/ debate ☐	I developed my spoken language ☐
	I learned with others ☐	I used digital technology to communicate ☐	I read and wrote in different ways ☐
	I worked with others using digital technology ☐		

Discuss two skills (above) that you intend to focus on more in the future.

_____

_____

_____

_____

Health-related activity

Chapter 02

Introduction

A big part of keeping your body fit and healthy is keeping your body moving! Regular physical activity helps keep your heart and lungs in good health, your muscles in good shape, and your bones strong. It helps you to feel better generally – it even helps you to study better at school!

We need to do at least 60 minutes of heart-pumping physical activity every day. This is called 'moderate to vigorous physical activity' – MVPA. This is just the minimum amount of movement we need to do to stay fit and healthy. The important thing to remember is that this doesn't have to be hard work! Physical activity is one of the most important fun things you can build into your daily life. You can be active on our own – by going for a walk or a run, dancing, or kicking a ball off a wall. You can be active with a friend – by playing tennis, pucking a sliotar over and back, doing tricks on a trampoline, practising long jump, or playing one-on-one basketball. Of course, you can also be active with a group of friends or with a team – by playing soccer, hockey, camogie, football, volleyball, or doing a group gymnastics routine. There are loads of ways to be active!

The important thing is that you are active, and that you find activities you can really enjoy doing. In this chapter, we will focus on the many really positive effects that being active has on your body. We'll look at how activity affects your heart, lungs and body temperature. We'll learn about the different parts of the body and the movements that add up to 'physical fitness'. Most important, we'll see that physical activity is fun, and it is for *everyone*. All you have to do is find the activities that are most enjoyable for you – and then do them!

Common terms

Physical activity	Moving your body enough to make your heart and lungs work a little harder than they do when you are resting
Intensity	How difficult an activity is, and the pace of it
Moderate to vigorous physical activity (MVPA)	This is about the intensity of the physical activity: moving your body enough so that your heart beats faster than normal, you breathe faster, and you sweat a little
Physical fitness	A combination of how well your heart and lungs can keep working at a hard intensity; how strong your muscles are and how long they can keep working for; your flexibility; and your body composition
Improvement plan	A plan you design to practise, monitor and develop a skill or ability over time
Goal	The intention or target you aim to achieve with your plan

Assessment tools

1. Rate of perceived exertion in PE

The facts

- When you are physically active, your heart and lungs have to work harder than normal.

- 'Sedentary' means sitting down, not really moving.

- 'Light' physical activity means you are working just a little harder than normal.

- 'Moderate' means you are working harder than Light, but not going as hard as you can.

- 'Vigorous' is when you are working nearly as hard as you can.

- To judge whether you are being active in the Light, Moderate or Vigorous zone, pay attention to your breathing, and how much you are sweating.

Task

When your teacher asks you, tick one of the boxes below for Activities 1, 2 and 3 to identify which intensity zone you were working in.

Intensity zone	Rating	Description	Activity 1	2	3
Sedentary		**Doing nothing** I am sitting down and watching TV.			
Light		**Really easy** I could do this in my sleep.			
		Easy I'm comfortable: I could do this pace all day.			
		Not so easy This is still easy-ish, but I am starting to feel a bit warmer and I'm breathing a little harder.			
Your daily 60 minutes starts here!					
Moderate		**Getting hard** I'm starting to sweat a little and breathe a little faster, but I can still talk comfortably.			
		Pretty hard I'm sweating more now and breathing faster, but can still talk.			
		Hard I'm getting a bit breathless now and I'm sweating. It's not easy to have a conversation.			
Vigorous		**Really hard** I'm even more out of breath. It's very hard to talk. Really sweating now.			
		Really really hard I'm almost out of breath: the most I could give now is a one-word answer.			
		On the verge I'm completely out of breath. I can't talk.			
		Unsustainable! I have collapsed!			

2. Measuring breathing rate and heart rate

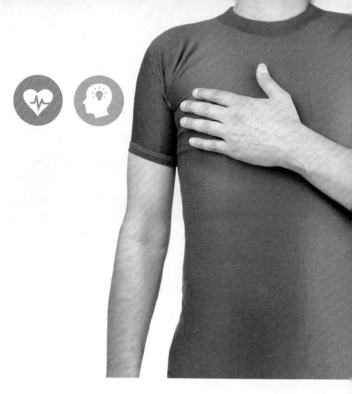

The facts: breathing rate

Your breathing rate is a measure of how many breaths you take in one minute.

To count your breaths:

- Place your hand flat on your upper chest and count how many times you inhale in a set period of time.

- Do your calculation, if you need to, based on how long you counted.

Task

When your teacher asks you, measure your breathing rate and write it in the table below.

Breathing rate (BR)	BR counted in ____ seconds	BR per minute
After Activity 1		
After Activity 2		

Calculation table for breathing rate and heart rate

Measurement duration	Calculation	Formula
60 seconds	None: the number you counted is the number of breaths/beats you had in one minute	None
30 seconds	Multiply the number of breaths/beats by 2	× 2
10 seconds	Multiply the number of breaths/beats by 6	× 6
6 seconds	Multiply the number of breaths/beats by 10	× 10

The facts: heart rate

Your heart rate is a measure of how many times your heart beats in one minute. This is also called a 'pulse rate'. You can feel your heart beating (your pulse) best at your neck (carotid pulse) or your wrist (radial pulse).

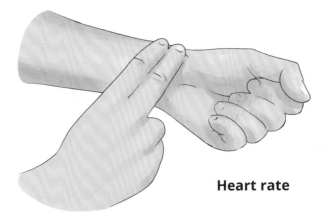

Heart rate

To measure your pulse:

- Place two fingers gently on your neck or your wrist, as shown in the pictures below.

- Count how many times you feel your pulse beating in the period of time your teacher says.

- Do your calculation, if you need to, based on how long you counted.

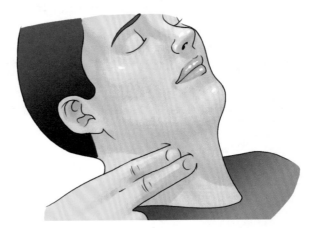

Task

When your teacher asks you, measure your heart rate and write it in the table below.

Heart rate (HR)	HR counted in _____ seconds	HR per minute
After Activity 1		
After Activity 2		

3. Effects of physical activity on the body as intensity changes

The facts

Your heart rate (HR), breathing rate (BR) and rate of perceived exertion (RPE) change, based on how hard or how easy the physical activity is.

Task

When your teacher asks you, measure your heart rate, measure your breathing rate, and note your rate of perceived exertion. (Remember the scale for this on p.33.)

Activity	Heart rate (HR) (beats per minute)	Breathing rate (BR) (breaths per minute)	Rate of perceived exertion (RPE)
Pre warm-up			
After warm-up			
After main activity			
After cool-down			

Describe what happened to your HR, BR, and RPE rates as the lesson progressed:

_____

_____

_____

_____

Why did this happen? Explain.

_____

_____

_____

_____

4. 'Physical activity' run

Task

Answer the questions below, by choosing true or false.

Listen to the questions as your teacher calls them out. Then answer by running to the **True Zone** or the **False Zone** of the court, as quickly as you can.

1. Physical activity is good for your body.

   (a) True   **(b)** False

2. To be healthy, I need to do at least 60 minutes of physical activity, five days per week.

   (a) True   **(b)** False

3. The healthiest way for me to meet new friends is to play computer games online.

   (a) True   **(b)** False

4. Being physically active can help my body to feel better.

   (a) True   **(b)** False

5. Being physically active can help my mind to feel better.

   (a) True   **(b)** False

6. We warm up before PE class to avoid getting injured.

   (a) True   **(b)** False

7. Physical activity helps reduce my risk of having a heart attack when I get older.

   (a) True   **(b)** False

8. If the intensity of an activity goes from fast to slow, it is probably a warm-up.

   (a) True   **(b)** False

9. Physical activity helps reduce my risk of getting cancer when I get older.

   (a) True   **(b)** False

10. Cooling down after an activity allows me to lower my heart rate.

    (a) True   **(b)** False

11. Physical activity is really only for people who are fit and naturally good at sports.

    (a) True   **(b)** False

12. Each of us can find a physical activity that we are good at and can enjoy.

    (a) True   **(b)** False

5. What I know about activity and the body

Task

1. How many minutes a day of moderate to vigorous physical activity (MVPA) do young people need to stay healthy?

    _____

2. What does 'moderate to vigorous intensity' mean?

    _____

    _____

    _____

3. How would you know if you are exercising at a moderate to vigorous intensity?

    _____

    _____

    _____

4. If you record your heart rate for 10 seconds, and count 12 beats, what is the calculation in beats per minute (bpm)?

    _____

5. Fill in the missing words.

    > blood, heart, faster, muscles

    Our _____ pumps blood around the body to our muscles.
    When we are active, our _____ do more work, and so they
    need more _____. To make this happen,
    our heart pumps _____.

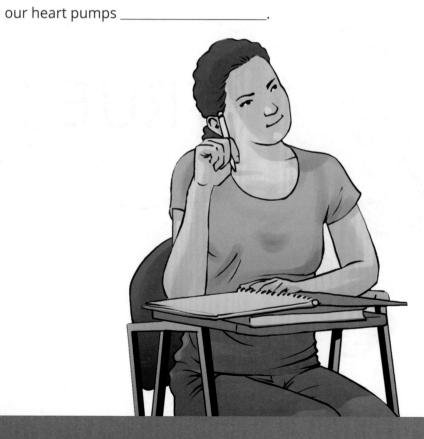

6. Fill the missing words.

> neck, neck, wrist, wrist, arteries

There are two simple ways to measure my pulse rate: one is to measure it at the
_____, and the other at the _____. This is because
_____ carrying blood are close to the skin at these two places,
so we can feel the pulse. The carotid pulse is the pulse at the _____.
The radial pulse is the pulse at the _____.

7. Circle the answer. Then write an explanation.

The fitter I get, the **quicker/slower** my heart will have to beat to pump blood to
my muscles during exercise.

Explanation:

_____

_____

_____

_____

_____

8. Label the muscles.

6. Muscles of the body

Task

Choose any sport you want. Then answer the questions below. You may know some answers already. You may need to research online for other answers.

My chosen sport: _____

1. What parts of the body are used most in this sport?

   _____

   _____

   _____

2. What injuries happen most often to players of this sport?

   _____

   _____

   _____

3. In terms of 'flexibility', which muscles should someone playing this sport focus on the most?

   _____

   _____

   _____

4. Draw a picture of someone doing one skill from this sport. Label **five** of the muscles most important for this movement.

   My chosen skill: _____ .

7. What I know about the components of fitness

Task

1. The pictures below show the components of fitness. Label each component.

_____   _____   _____

_____

_____

2. What is the difference between muscular strength and muscular endurance?

_____

3. How many times a week should a young person do exercises for flexibility and muscle strengthening?

_____

4. How can you improve your flexibility?

_____

5. Give an example of one activity you could do at home to:

   (a) Improve the strength in your arms

   _____

   (b) Improve the strength in your legs

   _____

8. My physical fitness profile

The facts

Physical fitness is really important for your health and wellbeing. To keep your body as healthy and fit as possible, you need to **keep track** of your fitness. If you find that you are doing well, you will need to focus on keeping up this level of fitness, even when you become an adult. If you find that you could improve on some of your fitness measures (which most of us can!), you will need to think about how you can improve. Then make those improvements happen!

Task

With your teacher's help, fill in the physical fitness profile below. Your teacher will do some fitness tests with you, and you will record your scores.

Remember: your fitness profile is just about you. It makes no sense to compare your fitness profile with anyone else's fitness profile. Just compare your scores *now* with the scores you get in the *future*, as you track your fitness levels.

	Possible tests	Test 1 Date:	Test 2 Date:
Cardiovascular endurance	Step test: heart rate afterward (bpm)		
Muscular strength	Grip strength (lb)		
Muscular endurance	One-minute press-up test (or modified)/min		
Flexibility	Sit and reach (cm)		

Test 1 reflection:

What component of fitness are you happy with?

_____

_____

_____

What component(s) of fitness would you most like to improve? Why?

_____

_____

_____

Write a plan for how you could improve over the next six weeks (while maintaining fitness in the other areas):

_____

_____

_____

_____

_____

Test 2 reflection:

Did you maintain or improve fitness?

_____

Why was this the case?

_____

_____

_____

What is your next fitness target, and how will you achieve it?

_____

_____

_____

_____

_____

_____

_____

_____

_____

9. Energy in, energy out 1: burning energy in physical activity

The facts

Being physically active is one of the most important things you can do to be healthy and to stay healthy at any age. Eating a balanced diet is just as important, however. And what you *eat* will, in many ways, influence how well you can *move*! A **calorie** is a unit of energy that fuels your body. The more active you are, the more calories (energy) you will use up. The less active you are, the fewer calories (energy) you will use up.

Task

It's time to do 30 minutes of physical activity!

- With a partner, choose some of activities from the table on p.45 and carry them out for 5- or 10-minute blocks.

- As you go along, record in the table the number of minutes you spend on each activity.

- When the 30 minutes is up, calculate how many calories you burned in each activity.

- Add the calories burned for each activity to record your total calories burned in 30 minutes.

> **Note:** The values for 'calories burned in **10** minutes' are given in the table. To find out how many calories are burned in **5** minutes, divide the value by 2!

	Calories burned in 10 minutes	Minutes of activity	Calories burned
Light activities			
Slow walk around the hall/pitch	23		
Throw and catch a ball	16		
Moderate–vigorous activities			
Moderate walk around the hall/pitch	29		
Badminton rally: medium effort	36		
Fast walk around the hall/pitch	37		
Aerobics: light effort (grapevine, V-step, etc.)	40		
Jumping a skipping rope	49		
Step aerobics: medium effort (low step)	50		
Basketball: shooting hoops	57		
Step aerobics: hard effort (high-step)	68		
Total calories spent in 30 minutes			

Did you notice any differences in your heart rate and breathing rate when you did the activities with the higher values for 'calories burned'? What were the differences?

_____

_____

_____

_____

Why did your heart rate and breathing change with the different activities?

_____

_____

_____

_____

_____

10. Energy in, energy out 2: physical activity and what I eat

The facts

- When you are choosing food to eat, and how much food to eat, think about how much energy you need – and how much physical activity you do.

- Different foods have different numbers of calories (energy) in them. Calories give you the energy you need to do all your activities during the day.

- To be healthy and active, you need different types of nutrients, and you need them in different amounts.

- The food pyramid shows all the types of foods you eat. It shows how much of each type you should eat every day to be healthy. You can eat smaller amounts of the foods shown on the higher shelves of the pyramid, and bigger amounts of the foods at the bottom. The foods on all the different shelves are important for us to be healthy – except for the top shelf!

- There are some foods that are bad for us in large amounts. These foods give us calories but they also contain things that are bad for our health if we eat them in large amounts – such as saturated fat, sugar and salt.

- Foods at the top of the pyramid are sometimes called 'junk foods' and they often come pre-packaged. Homemade foods and pre-packaged foods can be very different. For example, a homemade granola bar may contain very little sugar and be quite good for you, while a shop-bought granola bar may contain lots of sugar and be bad for you.

- You can eat the junk foods at the top of the pyramid, but it's best if you don't eat them very often: once or twice a week is enough. And if you do eat these foods, make sure to do extra activity to burn up the calories!

Task

- Below are some examples of packaged foods/junk foods that are easily available in the shops.

- Pick the **three junk foods** you have eaten most recently. Add the number of calories in these three foods, and write the total in 'Energy in'.

- Then pick **three activities** from the table on p.45, and do each activity for 10 minutes. Add the number of calories burned in these three activities, and write the total in 'Energy out'.

- Answer the four questions on p.48.

Junk food	Average calorie value	My three junk foods	My three activities (10 minutes each)
Granola bar (pre-packaged)	200		Calories burned in Activity 1:
Chocolate bar (30 g)	200		_____
Two chocolate biscuits	200		Calories burned in Activity 2:
Small bag of crisps	180		_____
Energy drink (500 ml)	200		Calories burned in Activity 3:
Can of cola	140		_____
Packet of sweets	180		
		Energy in =	Energy out =

47

1. Which is higher in your table: the 'Energy in' or the 'Energy out' calories?

   _____

2. Why are they different? What does this mean for you, if you eat junk food?

   _____

3. What do you think will happen to the 'Energy in' (calories) that you do not burn up in activity?

   _____

   _____

4. What do you think would happen if you did not eat enough calories to fuel all the activity you do in a day?

   _____

   _____

   _____

The Food Pyramid
Source: Safefood

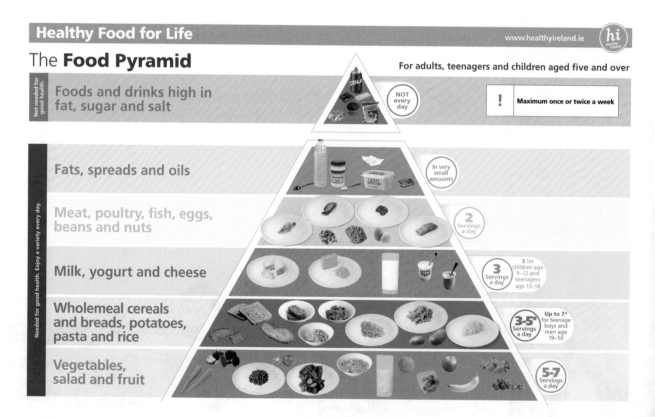

11. Planning a warm-up or cool-down

The facts

When you create a physical activity plan, you need to think about exactly what it is you will do. One of the easiest ways to go about this is using the **FITT** principle: **F**requency, **I**ntensity, **T**ime and **T**ype. The FITT principle highlights the four key things you need to be really clear about in a physical activity plan.

FITT principle	
Frequency	How often will you do the movement?
Intensity	How intensely will you do it? (How hard or easy will you go?)
Time	How long will you do the movement for?
Type	What type of movement(s) will you do?

Task

Work with your partner to create a warm-up or a cool-down for any sport you choose, using the FITT principle. Be ready to teach this warm-up or cool-down when your teacher asks!

> **Note**
> - Remember: a warm-up should start at a low intensity and work up to a high intensity. A cool-down should do the opposite.
> - A warm-up or cool-down should try to incorporate movements from the specific sport you are preparing for.
> - You can write and use diagrams to explain your plan.

Our chosen sport: _____

We chose a: warm-up/cool-down *(Circle one)*

Explanation of our warm-up:

End-of-unit assessment 1: My physical activity – plan to improve

The facts

To be healthy, you need to do at least 60 minutes of physical activity every day. This physical activity needs to be at a moderate or a vigorous intensity (MVPA). It has to be hard enough to make you sweat a little and breathe more quickly than normal! Also, it is important that you do not sit using a screen (e.g. TV, computer, tablet) – 'sedentary screen time' – for more than 2 hours a day.

Task

Think back over the past week. How many minutes of MVPA did you do? How many minutes of screen time did you have? Record the information in the table below.

My physical activity diary								
Date:		**Mon**	**Tue**	**Wed**	**Thurs**	**Fri**	**Sat**	**Sun**
Before school For example: MVPA: brisk walk to school for 5 mins Screen time: tablet for 15 mins	MVPA							
	Screen time							
During school For example: MVPA: basketball for 15 mins Screen time: computer for 30 mins	MVPA							
	Screen time							
After school For example: MVPA: swimming for 20 mins Screen time: TV for 60 mins, phone for 40 mins	MVPA							
	Screen time							
Total MVPA For example: 40 mins								
Total screen time For example: 145 mins								

- Did you make your 60-minute target of MVPA every day? Yes/No
- Did you have less than 120 minutes of screen time every day? Yes/No

My plan to improve

Think ahead to the next four weeks. How could you do **more physical activity** and have **less screen time**? Record the information in the table below.

My goal:		

- I will increase my physical activity by _____ mins every day.
- I will reduce my sitting time by _____ mins every day.

	What I plan to do	What might make it hard: challenges	How I can overcome this: solutions
Examples	Walk my dog for 20 mins after school	It could rain	Wear a raincoat and old runners
Mon			
Tue			
Wed			
Thurs			
Fri			
Sat			
Sun			

My evaluation

In the past four weeks, when you tried your plan to improve, did you find it difficult? What was it that made it easy/difficult for you?

_____

_____

_____

Were you able to do all the planned activities every day? Did you enjoy doing them? Did anything stop you from doing any of the activities?

_____

_____

_____

Did you manage to achieve your goal in terms of activity and sitting time? Why/why not?

_____

_____

_____

For the next four weeks, would you change your plan in any way? Why/why not?

_____

_____

_____

What did you learn about yourself from doing this activity?

_____

_____

_____

_____

End-of-unit assessment 2: My fitness – plan to improve

The facts

Physical fitness is really important for your health and wellbeing. To keep your body in its best condition, it is important to keep track of your fitness. You can maintain and even improve on your fitness all throughout your life.

When you want to improve in one area of fitness – for example, being able to run for longer ('cardiovascular endurance') – you need to train for it. But the *way* that you train is really important. You need to **plan** really well so that you can improve. There is a principle of training called **overload**, which is really important here.

Overload means that if you want to improve your fitness, each time you work out, you need to work your body a little harder than it is used to. Every week, you progress the activities so that they are a little harder, a little longer, and/or more intense. This allows your body to 'adapt', which allows it to improve! We can think about overload in terms of the FITT principle.

Overload, using the FITT principle: speed training example	
Frequency	Increase the number of times you sprint every week
Intensity	Increase the distances you sprint in your session
Time	Train for 5 minutes longer (or do five extra sprints) in your sessions
Type	Do some sprints up steps, rather than just on the flat

Task

- For this assessment, you will **record your partner's physical fitness profile** twice, with four weeks in between.

- After the first test, you will decide together what area(s) of fitness to work on. Then you will develop a **four-week programme**.

- After your partner has done the four-week programme, you will test their fitness again. Then you will talk with your partner to identify what difficulties they experienced.

- Remember: **fitness profiles are personal**. It makes no sense to compare your fitness profile with anyone else's fitness profile. Just compare your partner's scores *now* with the scores they get in the *future*.

Record your partner's scores for each fitness test.

	Test 1 Date:	Test 2 Date:
Cardiovascular endurance Test used: _____		
Muscular strength Test used: _____		
Muscular endurance Test used: _____		
Flexibility Test used: _____		

Plan to improve

Based on your partner's physical fitness profile, develop a four-week training programme for them. **Apply the principles of overload and FITT.**

My partner's four-week training programme

Goal for my partner:

- My partner will work on this component of fitness: _____.
- We will focus on this goal because: _____
_____
_____.

Exercises/activity

Describe the activities, how many days your partner should do them, and for how long. See the FITT and overload guidelines on p.53.

	Frequency	Intensity	Time	Type
Week 1				
Week 2				
Week 3				
Week 4				

Partner evaluation

Interview your partner to find out how well the programme worked. You could ask your partner some of the following questions:

- Did you find the programme easy or difficult?

- Did you enjoy doing the activities?

- Did anything stop you from doing any of the activities?

- Could you do all the activities?

_____

_____

_____

_____

_____

My evaluation

Based on your interview with your partner, and the repeated fitness tests, answer the questions below.

Did you (together) achieve the stated goal? Why/ why not?

_____

_____

_____

If you were doing this again, would you change the fitness programme? Why?

_____

_____

What did you learn about yourself from doing this activity?

_____

_____

_____

_____

_____

Strand review

In this chapter, you learned about:

- The positive effects of physical activity on your body ☐
- Moderate to vigorous physical activity (MVPA), and the importance of having 60 minutes of MVPA per day ☐
- Minimising your sitting time and inactive time ☐
- The components of health-related fitness ☐

- Measuring your physical fitness abilities ☐
- Warming up and cooling down, and how to plan a good warm-up and a good cool-down ☐
- FITT (Frequency, Intensity, Time, Type) ☐
- Overload ☐
- Applying the principles of training to design a fitness programme for your partner. ☐

Look back over the activities you completed. Tick the skills you used.

Managing Myself	Staying Well	Managing Information and Thinking	Being Numerate
I know myself better ☐	I am healthy and active ☐	I gathered and analysed information ☐	I estimated, predicted and calculated ☐
I made decisions ☐	I am social ☐	I thought creatively ☐	I was interested in problem-solving ☐
I set goals ☐	I am safe ☐	I thought about what I learned ☐	
I achieved goals ☐	I feel confident ☐	I used digital technology to access, manage and share information ☐	
I thought about what I learned ☐	I feel positive about what I learned ☐		
I used technology to learn ☐			

Being Creative	Working with Others	Communicating	Being Literate
I thought about things from a different point of view ☐	I developed relationships ☐	I listened to my classmates ☐	I understood some new words ☐
I put ideas into action ☐	I dealt with conflict ☐	I expressed myself ☐	I wrote for different reasons ☐
I learned in a creative way ☐	I cooperated ☐	I performed/ presented ☐	I expressed my ideas clearly ☐
I was creative with digital technology ☐	I respected difference ☐	I had a discussion/ debate ☐	I developed my spoken language ☐
	I learned with others ☐	I used digital technology to communicate ☐	I read and wrote in different ways ☐
	I worked with others using digital technology ☐		

Discuss two skills (above) that you intend to focus on more in the future.

_____

_____

_____

_____

Games
Chapter 03

Introduction

This chapter will help you to develop a wide range of skills, tactical awareness and a feeling of success, through participation in many different games. Whether your interest is in individual activities or team sports, this chapter allows you to excel in a safe and enjoyable environment.

Three main areas are covered in this chapter. The first section includes invasion games, such as basketball, soccer and Gaelic football; the second section includes court games, such as badminton and volleyball; and the third section includes striking and fielding games, such as rounders. There are assessment tasks to challenge your skills and knowledge in each area, as well as several general tasks that can be applied to all sports.

In Chapter 1 you were introduced to the idea of FMS (fundamental movement skills). In this chapter, you will have the opportunity to apply many of these FMS to sport-specific situations. So 'jumping for height' can now be applied to jumping for a ball, and the FMS of catching can be applied in many different ways in basketball, rounders or Gaelic football. Whenever possible, look back to Chapter 1 to check the technique of the various FMS that you meet in this chapter.

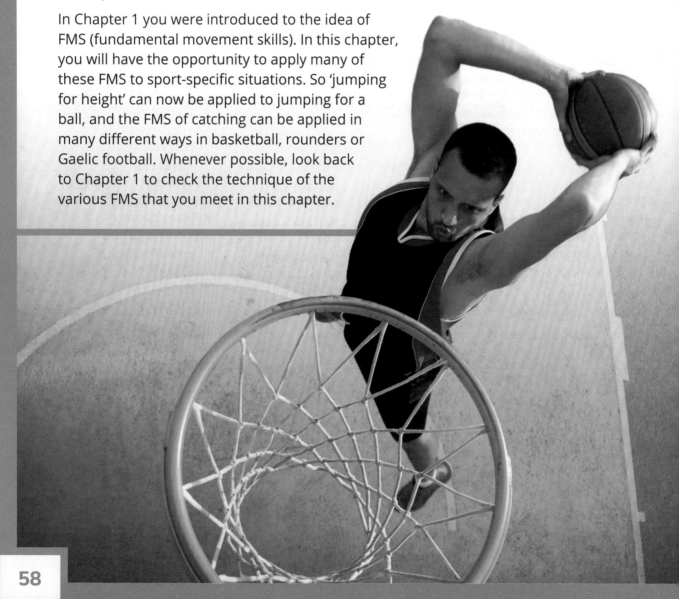

Common terms

Game-making	Designing a new game using criteria such as rules, scoring system, boundaries, game play, safety concerns and equipment needed
Sport-specific movement skills	Fundamental movement skills that have been adapted and progressed to meet the movement demands of a specific sport or physical activity
Fair play	Respect for the rules, and equal treatment for everyone
Offensive principles	Approaches to attacking play, and strategies to create scoring opportunities in a game situation
Defensive principles	Approaches to defensive play, and strategies to prevent scoring opportunities in a game situation
Heat map	A heat map is used to visualise a wide range of sporting data on a map specific to the sport
Technique	A way of carrying out or performing a skill
Technical point	A detailed description of one aspect of a skill
Reflection	The ability to think about something and comment on it honestly

Generic games assessment tools

1. Design a game

In this activity, you get to design your very own original game – complete with rules, a scoring system, safety precautions and game play. Building a game from scratch is a great way to understand all aspects of how a game is organised and played. It also helps you to better understand tactics and strategies of games you already play, competitively or socially.

With your group, brainstorm ideas. Don't be tempted to just take a drill you have used in soccer training or a game you played in the yard in primary school. Be original!

When you have chosen your game, discuss it with your teammates. Describe it under the headings below. Then find the equipment you need, and go play the game.

When you have mastered your new game, present it to your class and give them an opportunity to play it.

Task

Name of our game:

_____

How to play the game:

_____

_____

_____

Rules:

_____

_____

_____

Scoring system:

_____

_____

_____

 FMS Why not choose an FMS from Chapter 1 to focus on when designing your game?

Layout and boundaries (diagram):

Equipment needed:

_____

_____

Safety concerns and measures:

_____

_____

What did you learn about yourself while working as part of team to design something?

_____

_____

What did you find most challenging about the task?

_____

_____

What skills do you think are necessary to work in a team?

_____

_____

Note: If you need help with this, see p.49 for planning a warm-up or cool-down.

2. Games and a positive attitude

A positive attitude is vital in team settings and game settings. In sport, you develop abilities that you can apply in everyday life, such as the ability to remain positive, calm and focused in a challenging situation. When interacting with others, your attitude is even more important. Nobody wants to be spoken to harshly by their teammates and nobody wants to be the one feeling low at the end of PE. Sport is about fun! So enjoying yourself and, more important, making sure everyone else enjoys themselves should be the aim of the game.

Task

The table below has four boxes that show positive and negative terms and behaviours you may see when playing games. In your group, work with teammates to complete the table. Remember that everyone's opinion is important, so make sure all group members get a chance to contribute.

Complete the lists of positive/negative words, terms and behaviours.

Positive words and terms	Negative words and terms
'Well done!' 'Good pass!'	'Terrible!' 'Bad pass!'
Positive behaviour	**Negative behaviour**
Shaking hands after a game	Shouting at the referee

Case study 1

Johnny is frustrating Mary. Often, when Mary passes Johnny the ball, he drops it. Sometimes he also passes to a player on the opposite team. Mary does not go so far as scolding Johnny – but as the game goes on, she sighs, rolls her eyes, and her body language is extremely negative.

1. How do you think Johnny feels? Why?

_____

_____

2. What should Mary do?

_____

_____

3. List five characteristics of positive behaviour in sport.

_____

_____

Case study 2

Seamus and Imran play for the local U14 soccer team. They have a good team: in every game, every player gives it their all. However, the coach, Mr Noone, can get very angry. When the team loses, he gives out. After every game, he only talks about the things that went wrong – not the things that went well. Sometimes he picks out individual players to criticise. Mr Noone can also be very loud during games – telling players what to do, shouting instructions and getting very irritated on the line.

1. Is Mr Noone's behaviour OK? Explain your answer.

_____

_____

_____

_____

_____

_____

2. How do you think Mr Noone makes Seamus, Imran and the other players feel?

_____

_____

3. How should a coach behave?

_____

_____

_____

_____

3. Games: offensive principles

When looking at how games are won and lost, it usually comes down to two basic ideas: **attack** and **defence**. We often hear about the team that is excellent when they have the ball, but not when they are defending. Equally, we hear about the team that defend very well, but just cannot score. To be successful in any games setting, it is important to understand how to attack and defend effectively.

Offensive principles look at different approaches to attacking play. Every sport is different, but the intended outcome remains the same – to score. In badminton, you can force your opponent to the back of the court and then perform a drop shot. In soccer, you can launch a counter-attack. In basketball, you can perform a 'give and go'. In all these scenarios, you are using offensive principles to defeat the opposition.

Task

- Describe an offensive principle you intend using in a chosen game in your PE class.

- Outline why you think it might be effective and what situation you might use it in (draw a diagram if possible).

- Give it a go in the game setting.

- Then reflect on it afterwards.

Sport chosen: _____

Offensive principle chosen: _____

Description of the offensive principle (with diagram):

Did it work: Yes/No

What would you change next time? Why?

_____

_____

Design a drill or activity to practise the offensive principle you have chosen. Draw a diagram and explain how it works.

4. Games: defensive principles

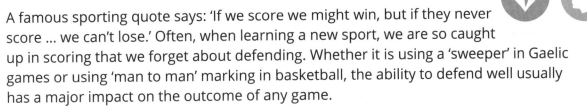

A famous sporting quote says: 'If we score we might win, but if they never score ... we can't lose.' Often, when learning a new sport, we are so caught up in scoring that we forget about defending. Whether it is using a 'sweeper' in Gaelic games or using 'man to man' marking in basketball, the ability to defend well usually has a major impact on the outcome of any game.

Task

- Describe a defensive principle you intend using in a game in PE class.

- Outline why you think it might be effective and what situation you might use it in (draw a diagram if possible).

- Give it a go in a game setting.

- Then reflect on it afterwards.

Sport chosen: _____

Defensive principle chosen: _____

Description of the defensive principle (with diagram):

Did it work: Yes/No

What would you change next time? Why?

_____

_____

Design a drill or activity to practise the defensive principle you have chosen. Draw a diagram and explain how it works.

5. Tracking my movement

Positioning is one of the most important concepts in sport. Almost all team tactics are based around the ideas of movement and positioning. Regardless of the sport, the position you are playing in and your ability to operate in that space has a huge impact on how successful you and your team will be. Most scoring opportunities in sport come from positioning errors on the other team – whether that is the defender caught out of position in soccer, the basketball player who did not track back, or the badminton player who did not approach the net in time.

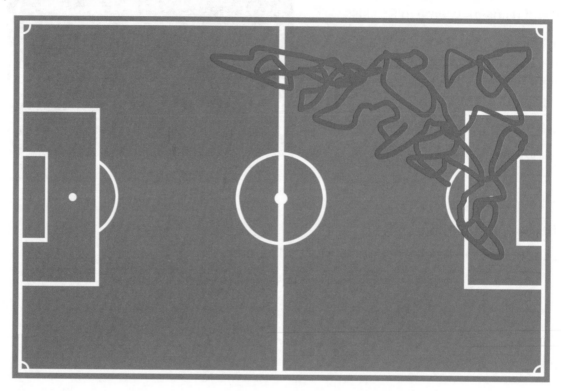

Task

- Draw a map of the court or pitch into the box on p.67. Then find a partner.

- While you are playing, your partner will take your workbook and track your movement, and you will do the same for them. There are two options for you and your partner to choose from:

1. Movement heat map: For a set period of time, your partner will follow your every move on the playing area by drawing it onto the map. The pen should stay on the map at all times, with your partner following your movement as you go. This will provide a good visual of where you went most often during the game.

2. Possession map: In this map, your partner puts an X every time you touch the ball, shuttle, etc. It is important that the X is put in the exact location the touch was made.

Choose a partner to work with

1. Ask your partner to fill in the map below.

2. Now work with your partner to answer the questions.

Heat map	
Sport:	Intended position:

1. What did you learn from tracking your partner's movement?

_____

_____

2. What did you learn about your own movement after viewing your maps?

_____

_____

3. Is there anything you will change about how you play the game because of these findings? Why?

_____

_____

_____

_____

6. Sport and mixed ability

In Maths class or English class, it is easy for us to understand mixed ability. Some people are just better than others at Maths. It's as simple as that. But when it comes to PE, and competitive sports in particular, we find it harder to understand and appreciate mixed ability. The most important value of PE class is that sport and physical activity is for *everyone*, regardless of ability or interest.

Task 1

You will work in a group of six to explore mixed ability:

- Design a mini-game based on what you are currently doing in PE.

- Add rules, a scoring system, boundaries and general play instructions.

- Write a description of your game in the box below and draw a diagram.

Task 2

Imagine that the mini-game you have design is too difficult to play for some members of the class.

- Work with your group to design a variation of the game, making it technically less difficult.

- Write a description of your game in the box below and draw a diagram.

- If you have time, brainstorm a name for your new game!

Task 3

Imagine that a student with a physical disability has joined your class. You can choose from someone with a visual impairment, hearing impairment or someone with limited mobility (e.g. wheelchair user).

- Redesign your game so that everyone, including your new classmate, can play it.

- Outline the changes you will make.

- Describe your new game.

1. Have you learned anything new today?

2. Do you have a different view on PE and sport in general? If so, why? If not, why not?

7. Fair play in sport

The idea of fair play in sport has received a lot of attention in recent years. FIFA has been promoting fair play in soccer since 1987, with a special award presented in recognition of behaviour that promotes the spirit of fair play. The Olympic Council showed that fair play was so important for the London Olympic Games that they produced a 'fair play coin'. In this task, we will see what fair play is all about.

You will need to do some research at home, discuss your findings with a group of classmates, and then choose aspects of fair play to focus on in PE in the coming weeks.

Task

1. List five characteristics of fair play in sport.

   _____

   _____

   _____

   _____

   _____

2. Which three characteristics of fair play are most important to you? Why?

   (a) _____

   _____

   (b) _____

   _____

   (c) _____

   _____

3. As a class group, choose one aspect of fair play to focus on for the next four weeks. Explain why the class group has made this choice.

   _____

   _____

   _____

   _____

   _____

   _____

   _____

   _____

   _____

Badminton

Badminton terms

Draw a line from the keyword to its description.

Keywords		Descriptions
Court		The area between the net and the short service line
Racket		The rear third of the court
Shuttle (shuttlecock)		The area into which the serve must be delivered
Short service line		A shot played softly to land just over the net
Fore (front) court		The playing area, measuring 44 ft × 20 ft (13.4 m × 6.1 m)
Midcourt		A basic shot in badminton used to send the shuttle to the backcourt
Backcourt		This is a line 6 ½ ft (1.98 m) back from the net that a serve must reach
Service court		The middle third of the court, after the short service line
Drop		An attacking downward shot, at an angle and with power
Smash		The object you hit with the racket
Drive		The piece of equipment used to hit the shuttle
Clear		A flat, fast shot that travels horizontally over the net

Badminton 1: Racket grip

The first step in playing badminton is to grip the racket correctly. This increases your chances of making contact with the shuttle. It improves the accuracy of your shots.

Forehand grip

The forehand grip is used to hit shots that are on the same side of the body as the hand you use to hold the racket (the forehand), and for shots around the head. To work on your forehand grip, set up your grip, using the self-check table below. Practise your grip by playing a rally with a classmate.

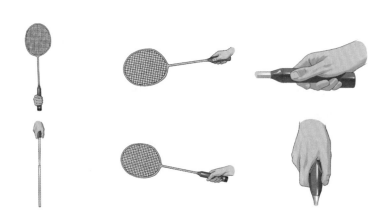

Backhand grip

The backhand grip is used to hit shots that are on the backhand side of your body. Your backhand grip is built on your forehand grip, so do not attempt the backhand grip until you are very comfortable with the forehand grip! When you have mastered the forehand grip, your teacher can tell you about the backhand grip.

 **Self-check** | Fill in the table below to assess your technique. Tick green for 'I've mastered it' or red for 'I need more practice'. Be honest and be strict!

Correct technique: Forehand grip	●	●
Do you hold the racket so that the handle points towards you?	○	○
Is the flat part of your racket sideways (perpendicular to the ground), not facing the sky?	○	○
Have you placed your playing hand towards the base of the handle, as if you are shaking hands with it?	○	○
Is there a V-shape between your thumb and your index finger?	○	○
Is the racket handle resting loosely in your fingers (for greater flexibility)?	○	○
Is the side (not the pad) of your thumb making contact with the handle?	○	○

Badminton 2: Overhead clear

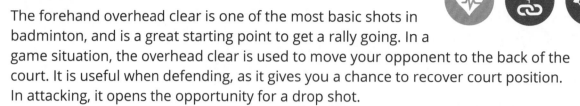

The forehand overhead clear is one of the most basic shots in badminton, and is a great starting point to get a rally going. In a game situation, the overhead clear is used to move your opponent to the back of the court. It is useful when defending, as it gives you a chance to recover court position. In attacking, it opens the opportunity for a drop shot.

For this task, you will work in a group of four: two pairs of partners.

- One person from each pair will try to maintain a rally, using the overhead clear.

- Their partners complete the table on p.75.

- When you are assessing the different points in the table, look at **one** item at a time.

- Try to view the shot technique from several different angles.

Even though the arm action moves in a different plan, many of the technical points of the overhead clear are similar to the FMS of throwing. You could review pp.10–11 and practise your throwing technique with a shuttle, then apply the action to the overhead clear.

Choose a partner to work with

1. Ask your partner to assess your technique and to tick 'Mastered', 'Nearly there' or 'Needs more practice'.
2. Then work with your partner to answer the questions.

Correct technique			
Is the forehand grip being used?	○	○	○
Is the body turned, standing sideways to the net, with the non-racket shoulder facing the net?	○	○	○
Does the body weight shift onto the rear foot?	○	○	○
Does the elbow bend and the wrist lock just before the racket swings forward?	○	○	○
Is the non-racket hand raised and pointing at the shuttle, to improve timing and balance?	○	○	○
Does the racket contact the shuttle as high as possible and in front of the body?	○	○	○
Does the elbow straighten as contact is made with the shuttle?	○	○	○
Is the wrist locked, and does it snap as the shuttle is hit?	○	○	○
During the shot, does the weight shift from the rear foot to the front foot, and does the racket follow through?	○	○	○

1. When is it suitable to use this shot?

_____

_____

2. When is it not suitable to use this shot?

_____

_____

3. In the scenario you mentioned in Question 2, what shot should you use?

_____

_____

Badminton 3: Smash

To analyse your smash technique, play a badminton rally with a partner for 2 minutes, asking them to tee-up a smash for you, when possible.

Ask a friend to record your rally from a number of different angles.

Watch the video clips, and tick the relevant traffic light for each technical point. It is important to watch the video clip at least once per technical point.

 Self-check Fill in the table below to assess your technique. Tick 'I've mastered it', 'I'm nearly there' or 'I need more practice'. Be honest and be strict!

Correct technique	🔴	⚪	🔴
Are you using the forehand grip?	◯	◯	◯
Is your body turned, standing sideways to the net with your non-racket shoulder facing the net?	◯	◯	◯
Is your body weight on the rear foot?	◯	◯	◯
Is your non-racket hand raised and pointing at the shuttle to line up the smash?	◯	◯	◯
Do you contact the shuttle as high as possible and in front of your body, using a strong throwing action (as if you are going to throw your racket high and forward through the air)?	◯	◯	◯
Does your elbow straighten as you make contact with the shuttle?	◯	◯	◯
Do you snap your wrist downwards at the point of contact, giving the shuttle extra power and downward angle towards your opponent's half of the court?	◯	◯	◯
Do you follow through and down with the racket, moving your weight from the back to the front foot?	◯	◯	◯

1. In a game setting, what conditions are needed to give you an opportunity to smash? (Draw a diagram, if necessary).

Badminton 4: Forehand drop shot

There are two main types of drop shots in badminton: forehand and backhand. The backhand drop shot is a difficult shot – so for this task, we will focus on the forehand. The drop shot is a deceptive shot used to catch out your opponent! You can use it to fool your opponent into believing you are going to use an overhead clear to backcourt – but instead tap the shuttle, rather than follow through, and send the shuttle gently over the net. For this task, you will work in a group of three.

- One person will attempt the drop shots.

- Their playing partner will maintain a rally, allowing themselves to be pushed backcourt to set up a drop shot.

- While this is going on, the third person will assess the drop shot technique, using the table below. Rotate positions each time the table is complete.

- When you are assessing the different technical points in the table, look at **one** item at a time.

- Try to view the shot technique from several different angles.

Choose a partner to work with

1. Ask your partner to assess your technique and to tick 'Mastered', 'Nearly there' or 'Needs more practice'.
2. Then work with your partner to answer the question on p.79.

Correct technique			
Is the forehand grip being used?	◯	◯	◯
Is the body turned, standing sideways to the net, with the non-racket shoulder facing the net?	◯	◯	◯
Is the body weight on the rear foot?	◯	◯	◯
Is the non-racket hand raised, pointing at the shuttle, to improve timing/balance?	◯	◯	◯
Does the racket contact the shuttle as high as possible and in front of the body?	◯	◯	◯
Does the elbow straighten as contact is made with the shuttle?	◯	◯	◯
Does the player slice or tap the shuttle as they hit it, reducing the speed of the racket-head on the follow through?	◯	◯	◯

1. The idea of deception is a huge part of the drop shot. Where, how and why would you use deception in other sports? Give three examples, using diagrams if necessary.

Note: In the forehand drop shot, the angle of the racket will determine the direction of the shot.

Badminton 5: Serve return tactics

In badminton, the serve has to be just right. If the serve is not long enough to reach backcourt, or if it is too high at the front of the court, this gives your opponent a chance to attack. In this assessment, you will learn how to gain a tactical advantage over your opponent by predicting where their serve will usually go.

To work on serve return tactics:

- Watch an opponent for a full game.

- Every time they serve, place a mark on the blank court below. You will need to predict (as best you can) where you believe the shuttle lands or is returned from. There are two ways to mark up your map:

  1. Place an X on the court position where the serve hits the ground.
  2. Place a circle on the court position from which the opponent returns the serve.

- Gather your data and analyse it.

- Challenge the server to a game. See if you can capitalise on the knowledge you have gathered to gain an advantage!

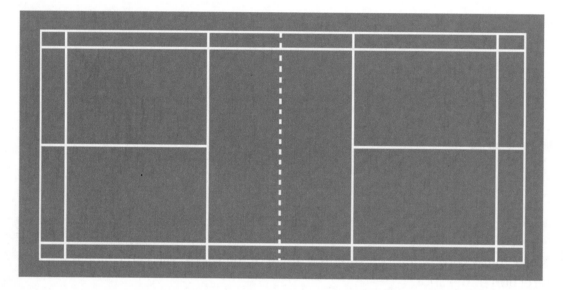

1. Were there any common trends to the serving you watched?

   _____

   _____

   _____

2. Could you use the data you gathered to your advantage? If so, how?

   _____

   _____

   _____

Badminton 6: Doubles positioning strategies – front and back versus side by side

When playing doubles badminton, two common tactical positions are used. If you watch the Olympics, you will see how badminton doubles partners approach the game. Some pairs will switch back and forth between the two strategies; other pairs prefer one strategy over the other.

Front and back

This strategy is often used when attacking: one player covers the back and middle court, while their partner covers the net. Front and back can be used when your opponents are on the back foot and you are pushing for a score (usually a smash or a drop shot).

Side by side

This strategy is more of a defensive tactic: players position themselves side by side in the middle of the court. This is a good position to defend from – it allows you to cover more of the court.

In this task, you will try out different positioning strategies, reflect on how it went and choose your favourite strategy.

To work on doubles positioning strategies:

- Play three games of doubles badminton (or play for a whole class).

- For each game, you and your partner focus on one of the strategies below.

- After each game, work with your partner to complete the relevant table below.

Strategy: side by side	Playing partner:
What did you like about this strategy?	
What were the limitations of this strategy?	

Strategy: front and back	Playing partner:
What did you like about this strategy?	
What were the limitations of this strategy?	

Note: To assess the mixed strategy, you and your partner will switch regularly between side by side and front and back, during open game play. You will choose side by side or front and back, depending on whether you are attacking or defending.

Strategy: mixed	Playing partner:

What did you like about this strategy?

_____

_____

What were the limitations of this strategy?

_____

_____

How did you and your partner decide to switch between strategies?

_____

_____

Favourite strategy

Which strategy was your favourite?

_____

Why was this your favourite strategy?

_____

_____

Can you think of any other strategies you might use during a badminton doubles game?

_____

_____

_____

Volleyball

Volleyball 1: Getting started

An average of 800 million people play volleyball weekly! Volleyball requires skill, strategy and teamwork. It takes time to learn the game, but it is well worth it. Master the basic skills, and you are on your way.

The ready position

First things first: you need to learn the ready position. In volleyball, players are sometimes stuck in the volley position when the ball comes low, so they cannot react in time to retrieve it. Similarly, players are sometimes caught low, in the dig position, only for the ball to come at head height. With their hands clasped for the dig, they cannot react in time to volley the ball. The ready position allows you to react quickly to a ball at any height and in any direction.

- Ask a partner to throw a volleyball to you at different heights and directions.

- Catch the ball, return it and repeat.

- After a couple of turns, assess one of the technical points in the table below. Then move on to assess the next technical point.

Self-check  Fill in the table below to assess your technique. Tick 'I've mastered it' or 'I need more practice'. Be honest and be strict!

Correct technique		
Do you have a low body position?	○	○
Are your feet shoulder-width apart?	○	○
Are your knees bent and inside the line of the toes?	○	○
Is your body weight forward, on the balls of your feet?	○	○
Are your back and spine straight?	○	○
Are your hands in front of your body?	○	○
Are your hands unclasped and ready to move?	○	○

Volleyball terms

Draw a line from the keyword to its description.

Keywords		Descriptions
Dig (forearm pass)		A serve that results directly in a score, usually hitting the ground without the opposition touching the ball
Underarm serve		A line 3 m back from the net, beyond which only the front court players can attack (jump)
Libero		A position that is low and relaxed but allows the player to move in any direction quickly
Overarm serve		A pass from a low position using the forearms, usually used in defence
Set pass (volley)		A pass made from above face height, using the fingertips, often used to set up an attack
Ready position		A serve using an underarm strike, usually with the heel of the hand
Ace		The action of jumping at the net, holding your hands high to prevent the ball crossing to your side
Spike (hit or attack)		A defensive player who can come into the backcourt to replace another player when the ball is not in play
Attack line		A one-handed attacking shot, hit with a downward trajectory to score a point
Backcourt		The area from the attack line to the base line where three players are positioned
Block		A serve from above shoulder height that comes in two types: float and spin

1. Are there any volleyball terms missing from the table above? Research online to find volleyball terms. Write and define any new terms you find.

_____

_____

_____

Volleyball 2: Volley/overhead pass

The volley is a two-handed pass played from just above the forehead. The volley has a high, slow trajectory in the shape of rainbow. This gives teammates time to get under the ball. The volley is also used to set up an attack in the form of a spike across the net. It is the most basic volleyball skill. If you want to keep a rally going with friends, you will use the volley.

Hand position

When volleying the ball:

- Form a triangle with your hands, using your thumbs and index fingers.

- Keep your fingers relaxed and slightly cupped in the shape of the ball.

- This will look and feel a bit like making 'Mickey Mouse ears' above your forehead. Try it!

Volleying technique

For this task, you will work in a group of three.
- Two of you will volley the ball to each other.

- The third person will assess one of you, completing the table below. Rotate positions three times so that everyone gets a chance to assess and be assessed.

- When you are assessing the different points in the table, look at **one** item at a time.

- Try to view the volleying technique from several different angles.

Choose a partner to work with

1. Ask your partner to assess your technique and to tick 'Mastered', 'Nearly there' or 'Needs more practice'.
2. Then work with your partner to answer the questions below.

Correct technique	●	○	●
Does your partner move their body quickly to get under the incoming ball?	○	○	○
Is the body facing in the direction of the intended target of the volley?	○	○	○
Do the hands make a triangular shape just above the forehand in preparation to volley (Mickey Mouse ears)?	○	○	○
Are the fingers relaxed, in a slightly cupped shape, and tilted back towards the forehead?	○	○	○
Are the knees bent in preparation for the volley?	○	○	○
Is contact made with the pads of the fingers (not the fingertips) in front of and just above the hairline of the head?	○	○	○
During the volley, do the arms extend quickly, with the wrist staying firm?	○	○	○
Do the elbows and knees straighten as contact is made with the ball, and extend towards the target?	○	○	○
Does your partner get back into the ready position quickly after performing the volley?	○	○	○

1. When volleying to a teammate, a high trajectory is important. Why?

   _____

   _____

   _____

   _____

2. Draw a simple sketch of the flight of a ball when it is volleyed from one teammate to another.

Volleyball 3: Dig (forearm pass)

The dig in volleyball is used when a ball is travelling too fast and too low to volley. The dig is a defensive pass that is most often used when receiving a serve or defending against a spike. The aim of the dig is to control the ball by taking some of the speed off the ball, using your forearms. A successful dig slows down the ball, which is passed with height, allowing a teammate to set up an attack.

Hand position

When digging the ball:

- Place your hands beside each other, facing up.

- Rest the fingers of your right hand on top of the fingers of your left hand.

- Bring your thumbs together.

- Ensure you are not squeezing too tight.

Quick feet for digging

1. It can be extremely challenging to get your body behind a fast-moving ball to dig it. This requires very quick feet. Can you design a drill or activity to practise quick feet? Use the space below to create your drill. Then work with your class to play each other's fast-feet activities.

Digging technique

For this task, you will work in a group of three.

- The first person will feed the ball to the second person, who returns it using a dig.

- The third person will assess the digger, completing the table below. Rotate positions three times so that everyone gets a chance to assess and be assessed.

- When you are assessing the different points in the table, look at **one** item at a time.

- Try to view the digging technique from several different angles.

Choose a partner to work with Ask your partner to assess your technique and to tick 'Mastered', 'Nearly there' or 'Needs more practice'.

Correct technique			
Is your partner in the ready position, waiting for the ball to arrive?	◯	◯	◯
Does your partner move their body quickly to get low and behind the flight of the ball?	◯	◯	◯
Are the arms straightened, held firm and away from the body during the dig?	◯	◯	◯
Does your partner adopt the correct hand position?	◯	◯	◯
Is contact made with the ball on the forehands, just behind the wrists (not on the wrists or the hands)?	◯	◯	◯
Do the arms remain locked, without bending the elbows during the dig, with very little arm swing?	◯	◯	◯
Does your partner face their intended target during the dig? Is contact made around waist height?	◯	◯	◯
Does your partner get back into the ready position quickly after performing the dig?	◯	◯	◯

> **Note**: When you practise the dig over and over, your forearms can become a bit sore. This is a good sign! It means you are doing it right: you are not using your wrist or hands.

Volleyball 4: Serve

The serve is used to restart the game. It can be taken from anywhere behind the baseline. The three main serves are: underarm, overarm and jump. We will look at the first two to see which you prefer.

Underarm serve

- Stand with one foot forward (on the non-serving arm side). ☐
- Place your weight on the back foot. ☐
- Hold the ball in your non-serving hand, and place your hand out in front of your body at waist height. ☐
- Gently toss the ball into the path of the serving arm. ☐
- Swing the serving arm through the ball, making contact with the heel of the hand or fist. ☐
- Ensure that the feeding arm releases the ball before contact. ☐
- As you serve, take a step with the front foot. ☐

Overarm serve

- Stand with one foot forward (on the non-serving arm side). ☐
- Place your weight on the back foot. ☐
- Hold the ball in your non-serving hand, and place your hand out in front of your body at chest height. ☐
- Hold the serving arm up, almost directly above the serving shoulder. ☐
- As you serve, take a step with your front foot and drag the back foot, transferring your weight forward. ☐
- Toss the ball high enough in the air to be struck at the highest point with the serving hand. ☐
- When you make contact with the ball, your elbow should be above your ear. ☐
- Contact the ball with the middle of a strong, flat, but slightly curved hand. ☐

1. Which serve do you prefer? Why?

   _____

2. Which serve do you think is more effective? Why?

   _____

3. Shoulder flexibility is important for the overarm serve. Can you think of a stretch to improve arm–shoulder flexibility?

   _____

Volleyball 5: Offensive strategies – finding holes

Volleyball is a very strategic game. The ability to identify an opposition's weakness and exploit it can be the difference between winning and losing in a competitive game. One side of a volleyball court is 9 m × 9 m – and this space is covered by only six players. So there is always some free space into which you can play the ball!

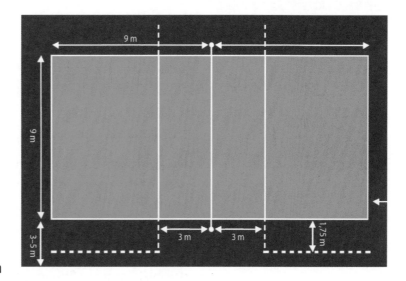

Often, teams will leave exposed the area behind the block or the back corners. The map (right) will help you to identify where an opposing team will concede the most scores.

For this task, you will watch a team (or both teams) playing a game of volleyball.

- On your map, every time a point is won, place an X on the court position where the ball hits the ground.

- You may develop a code to further analyse the game. For example: a score with a serve might be XS, a score with a volley might be XV, etc.

- At the end of the game, analyse your data.

- Work with a group of classmates to create a strategy for playing the team you observed. Then challenge them to a match.

1. Describe the strategy you intend to use, based on the data you gathered. Use a diagram to show your strategy.

Basketball

Basketball 1: Basics

1. Draw a line from the keyword to its description.

Keywords		Descriptions
Airball		A defensive strategy in which each player on the defensive team guards one person on the opposing team
Backboard		A defensive strategy in which players guard a specific zone or area of the court, instead of a specific player on the opposing team
Bank shot		This penalty, which results in a turnover, occurs when a player dribbles the ball with both hands; it also occurs when a player dribbles, stops dribbling, and then begins to dribble again
Carry		The rectangular piece of wood or fiberglass that is attached to the rim
Charge		A free shot given to a player after a foul or a technical foul; the player shoots from the 15-foot free throw line, while the rest of the players line up along the outside of the key
Double dribble		When a player shoots the ball and it bounces off the backboard and into the hoop
Fast break		This penalty, which results in a turnover, occurs when an offensive player with the ball runs into a stationary defensive player and knocks them over
Free throw		When a player from either team retrieves the ball and gains possession after a missed shot
Lay-up		A shot at the basket that misses everything and does not touch the rim, backboard or net
Man-to-man		A penalty, which results in a turnover, where an offensive player moves their pivot foot illegally or takes three steps without dribbling the ball
Zone defence		A shot taken close to the hoop, usually when a player is moving towards the basket
Rebound		An offensive action where a team tries to advance the ball to score as quickly as possible after a steal, blocked shot or rebound
Travel		This penalty, which results in a turnover, occurs when a player holds the ball excessively at the apex while dribbling

2. There are five traditional positions on a basketball court. These positions are listed below. Research each role and write a description of each role. Then place the corresponding letter in the correct circle on the half court map.

A. Point guard:

_____

_____

_____

B. Shooting guard:

_____

_____

_____

C. Small forward:

_____

_____

_____

D. Power forward:

_____

_____

_____

E. Centre:

_____

_____

_____

3. Which position best suits you? Why?

_____

_____

_____

_____

_____

_____

_____

_____

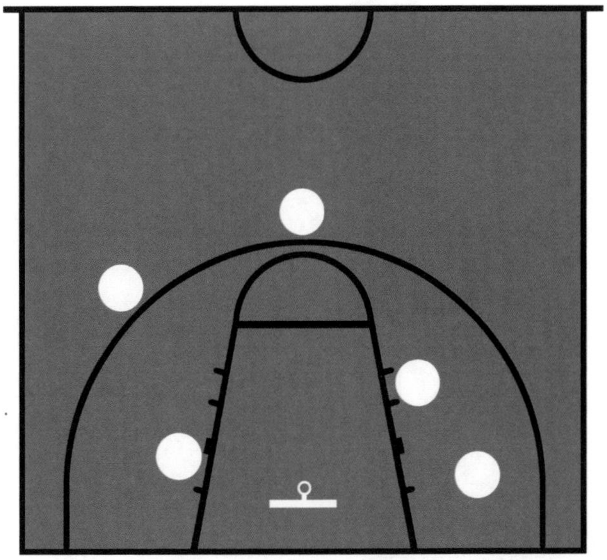

Basketball 2: Shooting challenge

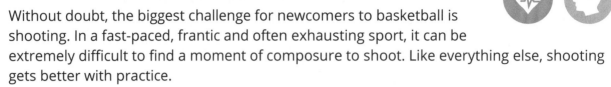

Without doubt, the biggest challenge for newcomers to basketball is shooting. In a fast-paced, frantic and often exhausting sport, it can be extremely difficult to find a moment of composure to shoot. Like everything else, shooting gets better with practice.

In this task, you will work with a partner to improve your shooting technique.

- Every week you do basketball in PE, your teacher will give the class five minutes of 'free time' to shoot at the beginning of class. Use this time to shoot as much as possible.

- Choose one of those weeks to complete the **self-check** section of the table on p.95. Observe how your technique is coming along.

- Choose a different week to ask a partner for help. Ask your partner to observe you and to complete the **partner check** section of the table.

- Separately, you will assess your shot success percentage. Use the table on p.96. On three separate occasions during the five-minute 'free time', you will count the number of shots you take and score (e.g. 15 scored from 27 shots). Use the data to work out your shot success percentage.

Shooting technique

Shooting technique	Self-check		Partner check My partner's name: _____	
	✔	✘	✔	✘
Eyes are focused on the basket at all times				
Feet are shoulder-width apart, with a slight bend in the knee				
The feet are slightly staggered: the foot on the shooting side is slightly ahead				
The shooting hand is behind the ball, with the fingers spread; this hand controls the force of the shot				
The non-shooting hand is on the side of the ball; this hand does not add force to the shot – it comes off the ball before the shooting hand				
The elbow of the shooting arm is positioned under the ball				
The legs generate the force				
The elbow and wrist extend towards the basket				
On releasing the ball, the shooting hand gently flops, the non-shooting hand stays to the side and does not influence the flight of the ball				
Follow-through is held until the ball hits the rim				
When performing a jump shot, the same steps apply, but the ball is released on the way up, just before the top of the jump; the player tries to land in the same spot				

Shot success percentage

$$\frac{\text{Shots scored}}{\text{Shots taken}} \times \frac{100}{1}$$

	Week 1	Week 2	Week 3
Workings:			
Answers:			

1. Try to work out your shot success percentage without a calculator. Give it a go: you can check it afterwards!
2. Did your success rate increase or decrease when a classmate was observing you?
    _____
3. Being observed closely can often put a shooter under pressure. What does this mean?
    _____
    _____
4. Does it occur elsewhere in life? Where? How do you cope with it?
    _____
    _____
    _____
    _____

Basketball 3: Passing clinic

The fastest way to move a ball around the court is to pass it. Try it and see for yourself. Ask someone to dribble the length of the court. At the same time, position someone on both end lines and one person on the half way line. You will see that three passes are faster than one dribble! In this task, we will attend 'passing clinic' to get your passing technique up to scratch.

It is your turn to become the teacher. You will work in a group of four.

- Each of you will choose one passing technique: chest pass, bounce pass, overhead pass or javelin (one-handed) pass.

- Take turns in teaching your group how to perform your chosen pass.

- As your group practises the pass, introduce the teaching points on p.98, one by one.

- Work as a group to help one another and give feedback.

- When you feel that a teaching point has been achieved, tick the box.

1. How did it feel to be the teacher?

   _____

   _____

   _____

2. What skills did you need to get your message across?

   _____

   _____

   _____

3. What was most challenging about the task?

   _____

   _____

   _____

For the **chest pass**:
- Keep your body standing square to the target. ☐
- Place your thumbs against the chest and your elbows out to the side. ☐
- Step towards the target. ☐
- Extend your arms fully and release the ball. ☐
- Ensure your thumbs are pointing down after release. ☐
- Your arms follow through, towards the target. ☐

For the **bounce pass**:
- Keep your body standing square to the target. ☐
- Place your thumbs against the chest and your elbows out to the side. ☐
- Step towards the target. ☐
- Extend your arms fully and release the ball downwards. ☐
- Turn your palms outwards and towards the floor on release. ☐
- The ball should bounce two-thirds of the way to the receiving target. ☐

For the **overhead pass**:
- Place your hands on either side and slightly behind the ball, spreading your fingers. ☐
- Raise the ball up to just above the forehead. ☐
- Keep elbows 90° and tucked in ☐
- Step towards the target. ☐
- Extend the arms forward to throw and release the ball off the first and second fingers. ☐
- Follow through with the arms. Keep the fingertips and palms facing the floor. ☐

For the **javelin (one-handed) pass**:
- Keep the body standing square to the target. ☐
- Hold the ball in one hand. ☐
- Start with the arm cocked behind the shoulder. ☐
- Step with your non-throwing foot. ☐
- Your throwing arm goes straight over the shoulder. ☐
- Your arm follows the ball in the direction of the target. ☐

 FMS This is a great opportunity to work on your catching technique (pp.6–7). Although the FMS of catching in Chapter 1 deals with a small ball, the same technique can be applied to a basketball.

Basketball 4: Heat map

In sport, the ability to move intelligently is often as important as the execution of skills. We have all heard of the sportsperson who was 'in the right place at the right time'. This task will track your movement on court, identify where you are in possession and what you do with the ball.

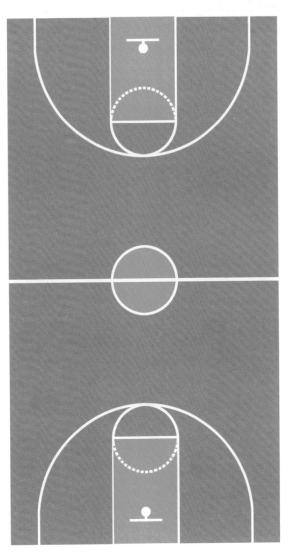

- Your partner will take your workbook and track your movement for 5–10 minutes of basketball.

- Your partner marks the heat map with these instructions:

    - Place an O on the court position where the ball is received.

    - If a dribble is performed, follow the movement with a broken line (e.g. _ _ _ _ _). Do this until a pass, shot or tackle is made.

    - When a pass is made, mark where the pass was made from, and identify whether the pass was successful or not (e.g. a successful pass gets ✔ and an unsuccessful pass gets ✘.)

---

1. Have you learned anything about your movement from this heat map?

   _____

   _____

2. Do you dribble or pass more? Why is this the case?

   _____

   _____

3. Analyse the data from the map and work out your pass success percentage:

   $$\frac{\text{Successful passes}}{\text{Total passes}} \times \frac{100}{1}$$

Basketball 5: Lay-up

Probably the easiest way to score in a basketball game is to use the fast-break offensive strategy. This involves getting the ball to your designated ball carrier as quickly as possible after a turnover, and breaking forward at pace. The ideal finish to a fast break is a lay-up, because the lay-up can be performed at speed.

Lay-up technique

To assess your lay-up technique:

- Ask a friend to video record you doing a lay-up.

- Take several recordings.

- Perform as many lay-ups as you can.

- Watch at least one recording for each technical point. Try to find an app that allows you to watch in slow motion.

- Using the criteria in the table on p.101, identify an area to improve in. Practise it, record it and repeat.

> **Note**: If you are right-handed, you will attack the right side of the basket. If you are left-handed, you will attack the left side of the basket. The technical points in the table on p.101 are for a right-handed basketball play. Just reverse them if you are left-handed.

Correct technique	Week 1			Week 2		
Do you dribble towards the basket, taking a line halfway between the rim and the right-hand side of the backboard?	○	○	○	○	○	○
Do you dribble to within two steps of the rim and hold the ball?	○	○	○	○	○	○
Do you step with the right leg (outside leg), then jump off the left leg (inside leg) towards the basket, while still holding the ball in both hands?	○	○	○	○	○	○
Do you take the ball in your right hand (outside hand) and extend up towards the backboard?	○	○	○	○	○	○
Do you lay the ball up and off the right-hand top corner of the red box and into the basket?	○	○	○	○	○	○
Do you land softly?	○	○	○	○	○	○

1. It is important to act responsibility when using videoing technology in class. Can you list three ways in which you can do this?

   (a) _____

   (b) _____

   (c) _____

 FMS The lay-up requires a great deal of muscular strength in the legs to generate power and height in the jump. Go to p.40 to explore the muscles involved in basketball.

Rounders

Rounders 1: Basics

Rounders is a traditional GAA game played with a bat and ball (sliotar). It is played in many Irish schools. A version of rounders is also played in the UK. Rounders is similar to baseball, which is very popular in the US. Rounders is a tactical sport that requires high levels of precision and skill-execution.

Baseball versus rounders

1.

Statement	True/False
(a) Baseball fielders use gloves, whereas rounders fielders use their bare hands.	
(b) Baseball bases are marked by small pads, whereas rounders bases are marked with poles.	
(c) Both sports were invented in America.	
(d) There is an Irish version of rounders and a British version of rounders, and these games have slightly different rules.	
(e) You can pitch overarm in rounders and in baseball.	
(f) A base cannot be occupied by two runners in either sport.	
(g) Rounders does not have a three-strike rule.	

Rounders terminology

1. Use the rounders keywords to complete the table.

Keywords in rounders						
Bad ball	Batting tee	Bunt	Fair ball	Foul ball	Fielder	Infield
Outfield	Pitcher	Short stop	Strike zone	Fair ground		Foul ground

Description	Keyword
The area between the lines drawn from home base to first base, and from home base to third base, which extend the full length of the field	
The area outside the lines drawn from home base to first base, and from home base to third base, which extend the full length of the field	
A ball hit by the batter directly into fair ground	
A ball hit by the batter directly into foul ground	
Area of fair ground outside the line of the bases	
The area over home base, between shoulders of the batter	
A fielder who plays to the left of second base or infield	
An adjustable rubber tee, used for batting practice and game play	
Area of fair ground inside the line of the bases (from first, through second, to third base)	
When a batter just taps the ball or pushes the bat into the ball, to make it roll in front of home base	
A player opposing the batting team, on the playing field	
The fielder who throws the ball for the batter to hit.	
A ball pitched by the pitcher which, in the opinion of the referee, does not pass over home base between the knee and shoulder of the batter	
Score:	/13

Rounders 2: Pitching

In rounders, pitching restarts the game. Pitching requires accuracy: the ball must pass over home base. Unlike the overarm pitch in baseball, the pitch in rounders must be an underarm action.

For this task, you will work in a group of three.

- Work in a triangle formation to practise your throwing technique.

- Set up a home base (a jumper will do).

- The pitcher stands 10 steps away and pitches to a catcher who stands directly behind home base.

- The third person will assess the pitcher, completing the table on p.105. Rotate positions three times so that everyone gets a chance to assess and be assessed.

- At the end, discuss any errors that were common to the group.

Choose a partner to work with

1. Ask your partner to assess your technique and to tick 'Mastered', 'Nearly there' or 'Needs more practice'.
2. Then work with your partner to answer the questions below.

Correct technique	●	○	●
Are the pitcher's eyes focused on the target?			
Does the pitcher grip the ball between the fingers and the thumb (not the palm of the hand)?			
Does the pitcher face the target square on?			
Are the feet staggered, with the leg on the throwing side behind the body?			
Is the weight on the back foot?			
Does the pitcher swing the arm back slowly and bring it forward quickly?			
Does the pitcher release the ball with a flick of the wrist?			
During the pitch, does the pitcher step forward with the front foot?			
Does the pitcher follow through in the direction of the target?			

1. Did you find it difficult to give your partner feedback? Yes ☐ No ☐
2. If your answer is yes, why?

_____

_____

_____

3. If your answer is no, did you find you were being too easy or too harsh on your partner?

_____

_____

_____

4. What is the purpose of feedback in a sporting context?

_____

_____

_____

Rounders 3: Batting and bunting

Batting and bunting is probably the most fun part of rounders, and it is also the most difficult. Hitting a ball with a round bat requires a great deal of accuracy and precision. A rounders bat does not have the flat surface of a golf club, hurley or racket. Therefore, a rounders bat has far less contact area on which to hit the ball. The skill takes a lot of practice. You will need to be patient, as you cannot simply burst the ball with power!

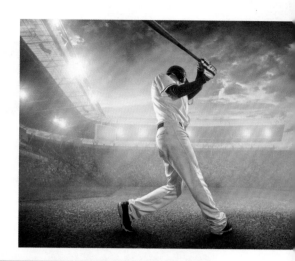

 Self-check Fill in the table below to assess your technique. Tick 'I've mastered it', 'I'm nearly there' or 'I need more practice'. Be honest and be strict!

Batting

This is a self-check task. There are seven technical points, so you should attempt to hit a ball at least seven times, ticking the checklist after each go.

Correct technique	●	○	●
Are you standing side-on to the target?			
Are your eyes focused on the ball throughout the hit?			
Are your hands together at the base of the bat? Does the hand at the end of the bat match the front foot?			
Are your feet shoulder-width apart, your knees slightly bent, with your weight placed on the back foot?			
Do you step forward with the front foot, and rotate your hips and shoulder during the hit?			
At the point of contact with the ball, do you extend your arms fully?			
Do you follow through the ball and around the body?			

Self-check Fill in the table below to assess your technique. Tick 'I've mastered it', 'I'm nearly there' or 'I need more practice'. Be honest and be strict!

Bunting

Have you tried the bunt? Bunting is when you just tap the ball or gently push the bat into the ball so that it travels very little distance in front of you. If there is enough space in front of you, bunting can be a useful way to get to first base.

- The steps for bunting are the same as batting, until you arrive at the strike. Instead of swinging the ball, you follow the steps below.

Correct technique			
When the pitch is thrown, do you turn to face the ball and slightly bend your knees?	○	○	○
Does your upper hand slide up the bat towards the hitting area?	○	○	○
Do you push the bat towards the oncoming ball with no follow-through?	○	○	○
After you make contact with the ball, do you run as fast as possible?	○	○	○

1. Which was easier: batting or bunting? Why?

   _____

   _____

2. Which do you think is more effective in a game setting?

   _____

   _____

 FMS Batting in rounders is the perfect time to work on the FMS of the two-handed strike. Why not work with a friend using the assessment tool on pp.20–21 to improve your technique?

Rounders 4: Analysing defence and offence

Offensive and defensive tactics and strategies are essential elements of almost every game we play. In this task, you will assess two strategies and analyse the results.

Offence

- When your team is infield and you are waiting for your turn to hit, take this time to sketch exactly where your teammates are batting and how successful they are.

- Track the flight of the ball, using a line on the map. Use the key to identify the outcome.

- Use the data to identify areas of the field where your teammates are having the most success batting.

X = Out

0 = No bases run

1 = 1 base run

2 = 2 bases run

3 = 3 bases run

4 = Rounder scored

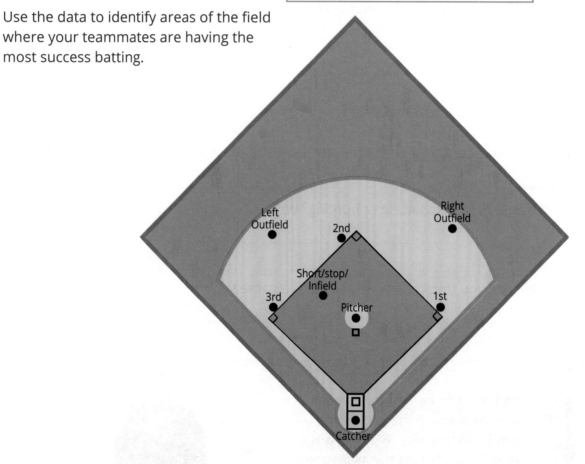

1. What trend (if any) did the heat map identify?

_____

_____

2. How did you use the heat map data to your advantage?

_____

_____

Defence

Find a classmate who forgot their PE gear today, and ask them to help you with this task.

While you are outfield, your partner fills in the heat map below, using the key (right):

X	= Out
0	= No bases run
1	= 1 base run
2	= 2 bases run
3	= 3 bases run
4	= Rounder scored

- Use the data to identify trends in batting. As the defending team, you can use the data to get the opposition 'out' more quickly.

- Remember to analyse the data between innings and reorganise your outfielders accordingly.

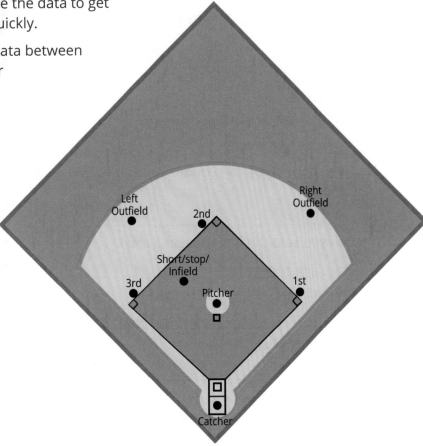

1. What trend (if any) did the heat map identify?

2. Could you use the data to alter your defence mid-game?

3. If so, was it a successful move?

4. Do you use tactics in any other sport you play? If so, explain how you do this.

Gaelic football

Gaelic football 1: Research challenge

1. How many players are on a Gaelic football team?
   _____

2. How many backs, forwards and midfielders are there?
   _____

3. A goal is worth how many points?
   _____

4. Can you hand pass a goal?
   _____

5. Can you hand pass a point?
   _____

6. How many steps can you take with the ball in your hands?
   _____

7. Can you solo the ball twice in a row?
   _____

8. What do the letters GAA stand for?
   _____

9. In what year was the first All-Ireland Football final played? Who won it?
   _____

10. When a ball is knocked behind the end line by a defender, the opposition can take the restart how far out from goal?
    _____

11. Who are the current All-Ireland football champions? What was the score in last year's final?
    _____

12. Which county has won the most All-Ireland football championships? How many championships?
    _____

13. How does a game of Gaelic football start, and restart after half time?
    _____

14. What is Hawk-Eye used for?
    _____

15. Which two of these are not tackles in Gaelic football:
    (a) Shoulder charge ☐
    (b) Open-hand tackle ☐
    (c) Closed-hand tackle ☐
    (d) Block down ☐
    (e) Take down ☐

16. What is a sweeper and what is it used for?

    _____

    _____

17. What is the difference between playing man-on-man and playing a blanket defence?

    _____

    _____

18. Why would a referee issue a black card to a player?

    _____

    _____

19. List five GAA grounds in Ireland and one GAA ground abroad.

    _____

    _____

20. Look at the final scores below. Calculate the scores in points, and identify the winner.

Team A	Team B	Scores in points	Winner
Mayo 2-11	Waterford 1-15		
Longford 5-17	Dublin 3-8		
London 4-16	Kildare 0-28		
Cork 3-4	Tyrone 1-9		
Donegal 5-5	Sligo 3-9		

Gaelic football 2: Travelling – bounce and solo

In Gaelic football, you cannot just run with the ball in your hands for as long as you want. You also cannot bounce the ball twice in a row. The rule states that you can travel for four steps with the ball in your hands, and then you must solo or bounce (hop) the ball. You can choose to never bounce the ball if you want, but a solo must be performed between bounces to stay moving.

> **Choose a partner to work with**

 Ask your partner to assess your technique and to tick 'Mastered' or 'Needs more practice'.

Correct technique: bouncing		
Does your partner hold the ball in both hands, with the eyes on the ball?	○	○
Just before bouncing the ball, are the fingers of the bouncing hand well spread out behind the ball?	○	○
Does your partner extend the arm and push the ball to the ground?	○	○
As the ball comes back up from the ground, does your partner extend both arms towards the ball? Do they meet the ball with the fingers spread, cushioning the ball into their hands?	○	○
Does your partner grip the ball securely and pull it back into the body with both hands?	○	○
When travelling at speed, does your partner bounce the ball well out in front of the body?	○	○

Correct technique: soloing		
Does your partner move the ball into one hand (the hand on the kicking side of the body)?	○	○
Do they step forward with their non-kicking foot?	○	○
Do they drop the ball onto the foot of the kicking leg, as it comes forward?	○	○
As the foot makes contact with the ball, does your partner flick the toe upwards and straighten the leg?	○	○
Does your partner extend both arms forward to catch the ball?	○	○
Does the solo come up no further than chest height?	○	○
Can your partner solo with the other leg also?	○	○

Feint and side-step

Remember that you will not always have the chance to solo unopposed in a nice straight line. However, you can use the skills you have already learned and apply them to beating an opponent in a game situation, using a feint and side-step.

A feint is a fake or pretend movement. A feint and side-step is when you give the impression you are going one direction, and then quickly go in another direction. The skill can be used in many other sports, such as basketball, rugby and soccer. The feint and side-step is well worth learning.

Self-check Fill in the table below to assess your technique. Tick 'I've mastered it' or 'I need more practice'.

Correct technique		
Do you run directly towards your opponent?	◯	◯
Do you feign movement to one side by leaning and stepping?	◯	◯
Do you push back off the planted foot to change direction?	◯	◯
Do you accelerate away quickly?	◯	◯
Can you give a quick glance in the direction you are faking? This can help to throw off your opponent.	◯	◯

GAA soloing and the body

Soloing is usually a high-intensity activity during a Gaelic football match. Soloing can also be paired with breaks while the ball is in another area of the field. This change of tempo has a major effect on the body. Use today's Gaelic football class to examine the effects of physical activity on the body as intensity changes. If you need help with this, see p.36.

FMS The feint and side-step is a sport-specific development of the FMS of dodging. Go to pp.8–9 to improve your dodging technique.

Gaelic football 3: Hand pass

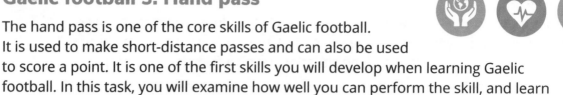

The hand pass is one of the core skills of Gaelic football. It is used to make short-distance passes and can also be used to score a point. It is one of the first skills you will develop when learning Gaelic football. In this task, you will examine how well you can perform the skill, and learn how to apply it to a game scenario.

Get a ball and video record yourself practising your hand passing against a wall.

Self-check Fill in the table below to assess your technique. Tick 'I've mastered it', 'I'm nearly there' or 'I need more practice'. Be honest and be strict!

Hand passing

Correct technique			
Do you hold the ball in your non-striking hand, in front of your body?	○	○	○
Do you swing back, then extend forward the striking hand?	○	○	○
Do you lean forward and strike through the middle of the ball with an open hand (or with the fist – for a fist pass)?	○	○	○
Do you follow through in the direction of the pass?	○	○	○
Do you keep your eyes on the ball throughout the striking action?	○	○	○

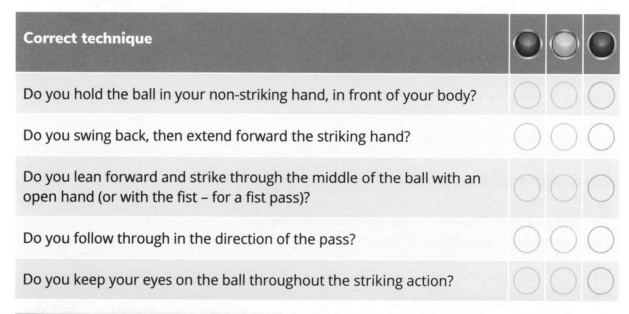

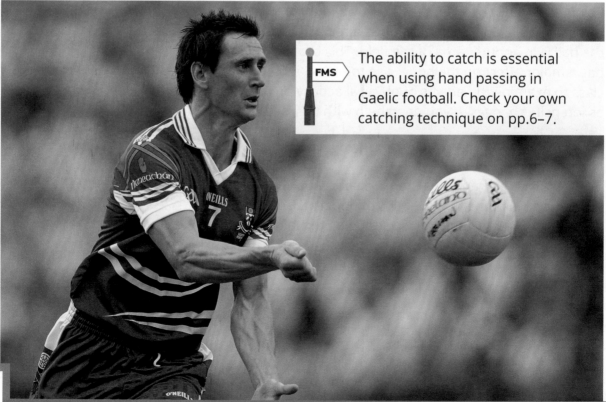

FMS The ability to catch is essential when using hand passing in Gaelic football. Check your own catching technique on pp.6–7.

1. Work in a group of six. Design a mini-game to practise hand passing.
   The game design should include:
   - A scoring system
   - Boundaries and a restart procedure
   - Rules to play the game
   - Any safety concerns.

Draw the game and describe it below.

Gaelic football 4: Kicking clinic

It is said that a game of the original version of Gaelic football may have involved hundreds of people kicking a ball for miles around the countryside, and stopping every now and then for a wrestling session! Wrestling is not part of the modern game; however, the skill of kicking is still a core element. In this task, you will work through the technical points for three different Gaelic football kicks: punt kick, hook kick and swerve kick.

Choose a partner to work with

1. Ask your partner to assess your technique and to tick 'Mastered', 'Nearly there' or 'Needs more practice' in the tables on pp.116–117.
2. Then work with your partner to answer the questions on p.118.

Punt kick

Correct technique			
Is the ball held firmly with both hands?	○	○	○
Is the ball then placed in the hand on the kicking side of the body?	○	○	○
Does the player keep their head down and eyes over the ball throughout?	○	○	○
Does the player step forward with the non-kicking foot?	○	○	○
Is the ball dropped onto the kicking foot, as the foot comes forward?	○	○	○
Is the ball kicked with the instep of the foot?	○	○	○
Does the player keep the toes pointed, and follow through in the direction of the target?	○	○	○

FMS ⟩ The punt, swerve and hook kicks are all sport-specific developments of the FMS of kicking. Why not work on your kicking technique, using the self-check on pp.14–15?

Hook kick

Correct technique	●	●	●
Is the ball held firmly with both hands, with the shoulder of the non-kicking leg facing towards the target?	○	○	○
Is the ball then placed in the hand on the kicking side of the body?	○	○	○
Does the player step forward with the non-kicking foot?	○	○	○
Is the ball dropped onto the kicking foot, as the foot comes forward?	○	○	○
Is the ball kicked with the inside of the foot?	○	○	○
Does the player follow through in the direction of the target, with their toes facing up (not pointed)?	○	○	○

Swerve kick

Correct technique	●	●	●
Does the player face slightly across the goal or intended target?	○	○	○
Does the player keep their head down and eyes on the ball throughout?	○	○	○
Does the player hold the ball firmly with both hands?	○	○	○
Does the player place the ball in the hand on the kicking side of the body, and extend the other arm out to the side (to help with balance)?	○	○	○
Does the player step forward with the non-kicking foot?	○	○	○
Is the ball dropped onto the kicking foot, as the foot comes forward?	○	○	○
Is the ball kicked with the outside of the foot (to swerve it)?	○	○	○
Does the player keep the toes pointed, and follow through in the direction of the target?	○	○	○

1. After trying all three kicks, which did you find easiest? Why?

   _____

   _____

2. Which kick did you find most difficult? Why?

   _____

   _____

3. For each kick, list one scenario in which you would use it in a game setting.
   • Punt kick:

   _____

   • Hook kick:

   _____

   • Swerve kick:

   _____

4.

   • Ask your partner to listen as you read, in random order, the answers (scenarios) you gave for Question 3.

   • Ask your partner to decide which kick they would use in each scenario.

   • Discuss any scenarios you do not agree on.

Gaelic football 5: Sport and the community

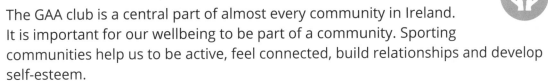

The GAA club is a central part of almost every community in Ireland. It is important for our wellbeing to be part of a community. Sporting communities help us to be active, feel connected, build relationships and develop self-esteem.

Task 1

In this task, you will profile a GAA club (or any other sports club) in your community. Answer the questions below to give an overview of the club and the role it plays in the lives of the people it serves.

Name of club: _____

Community it serves: _____

_____

Sport played: _____

_____

Year the club was founded: _____

_____

My involvement in the club:

_____

_____

_____

Task 2

Interview one **non-playing** member of the club. Design five questions in advance. These questions should help you to get a better idea of how the club runs, how many people are involved in running it, and what the person's role involves.

Question 1: _____

_____

Response: _____

_____

_____

Question 2: _____

_____

Response: _____

_____

_____

Question 3: _____

_____

Response: _____

_____

_____

Question 4: _____

_____

Response: _____

_____

_____

Question 5: _____

_____

Response: _____

_____

_____

Task 3

Interview one **playing** member of the club. Design five questions in advance. These questions should help you to get a better idea of how the club runs, how many people are involved in running it, and what the person's role involves.

Question 1: _____

_____

Response: _____

_____

_____

Question 2: _____

_____

Response: _____

_____

_____

Question 3: _____

_____

Response: _____

_____

_____

Question 4: _____

_____

Response: _____

_____

_____

Question 5: _____

_____

Response: _____

_____

_____

Reflection

After completing the interviews, do you believe the club contributes positively to the local community? Explain your answer.

_____

_____

_____

Soccer

Soccer 1: Coach for a day

In this task, it is your turn to become the coach. The traditional view of the coach is that he or she is the person who picks the team. In reality, there is a whole lot more involved in the role. Try this activity to find out for yourself.

You will work in a group of six:

- Choose six skills or tactical strategies in soccer (e.g. shooting, corners, offside or dribbling).

- Write each skill on a piece of paper and place them in a hat.

- Each person will choose one piece of paper from the hat.

- The skill/strategy you draw from the hat is the skill/strategy you will coach for 5 minutes next week.

- To prepare for your coaching session, complete the table below.

Name of skill/strategy:
Equipment needed:
Plan for coaching session: _____ _____ _____

Diagram of coaching activity:

1. Did you enjoy coaching?

   _____

2. What personal skills do you need as a coach?

   _____

   _____

3. Did your behaviour as a player change in the coaching sessions that came after your session as coach?

   _____

Soccer 2: Skills clinic

Versions of soccer date back 2,000 years in places such as China, Greece, Rome and Central America. However, the game we know today was established in England in 1863. In the modern game, we no longer kick a pig's bladder around the field! Many skills of the older version of the game have survived, however. In this task, you will assess these core skills.

Choose a partner to work with

1. Ask your partner to assess your technique and to tick 'Perfect', 'Good' or 'Needs work'.

2. Then work with your partner to answer the questions on p.125.

Dribbling: Technical points	Perfect	Good	Needs work
Points values	3	2	1
Eyes are focused on the ball			
Head comes up when possible to assess options			
Soft touches with the inside and outside of the foot			
Arms out for balance			
Keeps the ball close when dribbling slowly			
Pushes the ball further in front when sprinting			
Total score for dribbling			

Heading: Technical points	Perfect	Good	Needs work
Points values	3	2	1
Feet are shoulder-width apart and staggered, body has balanced centre of gravity			
Neck stays stiff – the back or waist is used to move towards the ball			
Eyes are open			
Mouth is closed			
Header is made with the forehead, between the hairline and eyebrows			
Bottom half of the ball is hit to go up; top half of the ball is hit to go down			
Total score for heading			

Shooting: Technical points	Perfect	Good	Needs work
Points values	3	2	1
Looks up to observe the goalkeeper's position			
Selects the correct technique for the situation: a side-footed shot for accuracy, or an instep (laces) shot for power			
The non-kicking foot is beside the ball			
Keeps the eyes on the ball throughout			
Keeps the body over the ball			
Makes contact with the middle of the ball and follows through			
Total score for shooting			

Overall score (dribbling + heading + shooting) = _____

1. What skill did you do well in? Why is this?

_____

_____

_____

2. What skill most needs improvement? Describe a plan to improve it, using a diagram.

_____

_____

_____

FMS When heading, it is important to jump as high as you can to meet the ball. Work with a partner to assess your jumping for height technique. See pp.16–17.

FMS Need to work on your kicking technique? Use the self-check on pp.14–15 to improve your technique.

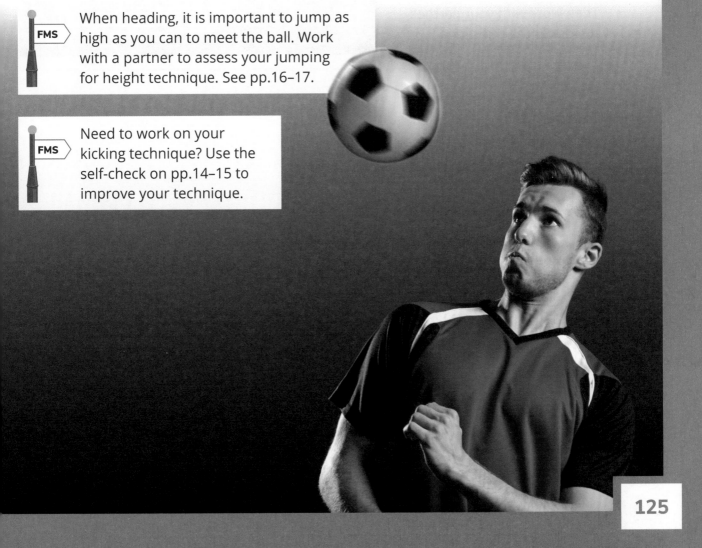

Soccer 3: Positional play

Probably the biggest difference between informal play (a kick-around with friends) and formal play (a competitive match) is the concept of positional play. When watching professional players, we do not identify them as just 'attacker' or 'defender', we talk about 'right wingers', 'left full-backs', etc.

For this task:

- You will play in a position of your choice.

- Your partner will take your workbook and track your movement.

- Ask your partner to complete the heat map. They will keep their pen on the map at all times, moving it to mirror your movement on the pitch.

- Then work with your partner to answer the questions.

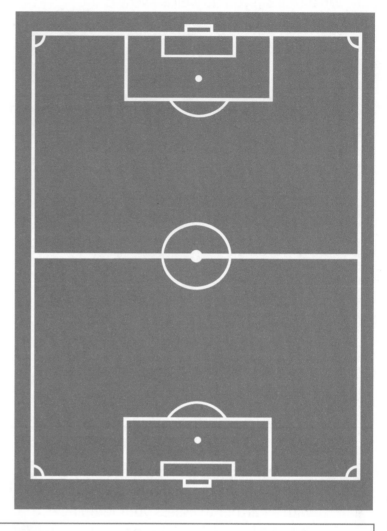

Name: _____

Position played: _____

1. Do you think the heat map is accurate? Yes/No

2. How well do you feel you played your position?

   _____

   _____

3. For what reasons did you leave your position?

   _____

   _____

4. Did those around you stay in their positions? What happens if one or more players do not play in their positions?

   _____

   _____

End-of-unit assessment 1: My sporting event

We have all watched major sporting events, whether it is the FIFA World Cup, the Six Nations Championships or the Olympic Games. But do we really appreciate the planning, organisation and work that goes into these competitions? This task gives you a behind-the-scenes look at sporting event management: you will organise, run and reflect on an event of your choice.

- You will work in a group of six to plan, run and evaluate an event.

- Choose a sport and an event title. (Your teacher will approve these first.)

- Record the statistics from the games played.

- Complete Tasks 1–7 below.

Event title

_____

Event managers

1. _____ 2. _____

3. _____ 4. _____

5. _____ 6. _____

Task 1: Choosing roles

Each member of the group will lead at least one aspect of the event. With your group, brainstorm the roles you think are necessary to run a successful sporting event. Examples of roles include:

- Fixtures Coordinator
- Timekeeper
- Scorekeeper
- Head of Refereeing
- Statistics

- Spokesperson
- Posters, Advertising and Branding
- Team Liaison Officer (to include team selection)
- Safety Officer (to include layout of sporting area and first aid)

Roles chosen

1. Leader: _____

2. Role _____
   Student name: _____

3. Role _____
   Student name: _____

MY EVENT

4. Role _____
   Student name: _____

5. Role _____
   Student name: _____

6. Role _____
   Student name: _____

Task 2: The event

Write a brief description of the event. Include information on:

- Timeline of activities
- Space required
- Set-up needed
- Scoring system used
- Any other relevant information.

Use a diagram, where possible.

Task 3: Exploring my role

Write about the role you have chosen to undertake.

Event management role: _____

1. Describe the role.

   _____
   _____
   _____

2. List the duties you will perform.

   _____
   _____
   _____
   _____
   _____

3. Why did you choose this role?

   _____
   _____

Task 4: My checklist

Before the event, design a checklist of the jobs you need to do (a) before and (b) during the event. Tick these off as you complete them. Remember: you are the leader in your area, but that does not mean you must do all the work yourself! Call on other group members for help, if you need it.

1. _____ ☐

2. _____ ☐

3. _____ ☐

4. _____ ☐

5. _____ ☐

6. _____ ☐

Task 5: How did the event go?

Answer the questions below to reflect on the overall success of the event.

1. List three things about the event that went well.

   _____

   _____

   _____

2. List three things you would change if you had the chance to run the event again.

   _____

   _____

   _____

3. Did the group work well as a team? List three elements of good teamwork that you noticed.

   _____

   _____

   _____

4. If you could give three pieces of advice to someone organising an event in the future, what would they be?

   _____

   _____

   _____

Possible classroom-based assessments

129

Task 6: How did I do?

Reflect on your role during the event and examine the skills you used.

1. Do you think that you carried out your role within the event successfully? Why/why not?

   _____

   _____

   _____

2. What personal skills did you use when coordinating your part of the event?

   _____

   _____

   _____

3. Did you help other members of your group during the event? If so, how?

   _____

   _____

   _____

Task 7: Beyond PE class

Answer the questions below to reflect on some of the skills you used during the event.

1. List three skills you used during the event. For each skill, explain where it could easily be used in other areas of your everyday life.

   (a) _____

   _____

   _____

   _____

   (b) _____

   _____

   _____

   _____

   (c) _____

   _____

   _____

   _____

possible CBA **End-of-unit assessment 2: My sporting profile**

This task gives you the opportunity to showcase a sport you enjoy playing. You will discuss how you got involved, why you like it, how people train and prepare for it, who you look up to and how you participate in the sport. You can learn a lot by looking at your sport from different angles.

Task 1: My sport

Outline the sport you have chosen to profile: _____

1. Why did you chose this sport?

   _____

   _____

2. How long you have been involved in it?

   _____

3. What do you like about it?

   _____

   _____

4. Can you share any other relevant information?

   _____

   _____

   _____

Task 2: How I prepare for my sport

Sport today can often require a great deal of commitment. In this section, describe how you prepare for participation in your sport.

1. Describe a typical training session that you do for your sport:

    _____

    _____

    _____

2. Do you have to eat (or avoid eating) any particular foods when you are preparing for your sport? Explain.

    _____

    _____

    _____

3. Are there any lifestyle choices you take because of your involvement in the sport (e.g. sleeping habits or socialising).

    _____

    _____

    _____

Task 3: Overview of a skill

Choose one skill from your sport. Describe, with use of a diagram, how you would develop this skill in a training session.

_____

_____

_____

_____

_____

Task 4: My sporting role model

When we think about our sporting idols, names such as Usain Bolt, Serena Williams or Joe Canning can come to mind. Often, we also admire sportspeople we know personally (e.g. an adult in our local sports club). For this task, you will design a questionnaire and conduct an interview with a sporting role model from your local community.

- Use the box below to brainstorm ideas for questions you might ask during the interview.

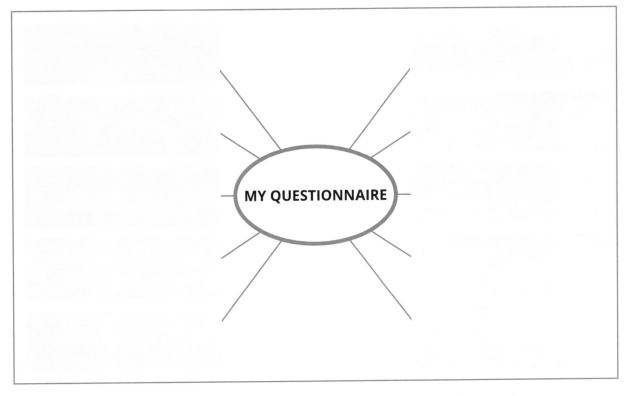

MY QUESTIONNAIRE

- Choose the interview questions you will ask, and write them in the questionnaire on pp.134–135.

- Set up a meeting and conduct your interview. Ensure that your parent/guardian accompanies you.

Questionnaire

Sportsperson interviewed: _____

Date: _____

Question 1: _____

_____

Response: _____

_____

_____

Question 2: _____

_____

Response: _____

_____

_____

Question 3: _____

_____

Response: _____

_____

_____

Question 4: _____

_____

Response: _____

_____

_____

Question 5: _____

_____

Response: _____

_____

_____

Question 6: _____

_____

Response: _____

_____

_____

Question 7: _____

Response: _____

_____

Question 8: _____

Response: _____

_____

Question 9: _____

Response: _____

_____

Question 10: _____

Response: _____

_____

Reflect on how your interview went.

1. Did you learn anything interesting about the sportsperson?

_____

_____

_____

_____

2. Did you learn anything that could benefit your participation in the sport? Explain.

_____

_____

_____

_____

_____

Task 5: My performance

For this part of the task, you will ask a friend to video you playing your sport. You will need footage of yourself in an attacking role, in a defensive role and using a range of different skills. Once you have gathered the data, watch the video, reflect on your performance and answer the questions below.

1. Describe a defensive situation during the game. What was your role and how did it play out?

   _____

   _____

   _____

   _____

2. Would you change anything if you were in the situation again?

   _____

   _____

3. Describe an offensive (attacking) situation during the game. What was your role and how did it play out?

   _____

   _____

   _____

   _____

4. Would you change anything if you were in the situation again?

   _____

   _____

5. List five skills you used during the game. Outline what each skill was used for.

   (a) _____

   _____

   (b) _____

   _____

   (c) _____

   _____

   (d) _____

   _____

   (e) _____

   _____

Strand review
In this chapter, you learned about:

- Designing a game ☐
- Defensive and offensive principles ☐
- Giving feedback to a classmate ☐
- Organising an event ☐
- Conducting an interview ☐
- Analysing movement and performance using a heat map ☐
- Applying FMS to a range of sport-specific movement skills ☐
- The muscles used in a sport of your choice ☐
- A sport in your community ☐

- Working in a team setting ☐
- Behaving as a coach ☐
- Positive and negative attitudes in sport ☐
- Using a warm-up or cool-down in a sport you play ☐
- Fair play ☐
- Varying a game/activity to cater for mixed ability ☐
- Playing divided court games ☐
- Playing invasion games ☐
- Playing striking and fielding games. ☐

Look back over the activities you completed. Tick the skills you used.

Managing Myself	Staying Well	Managing Information and Thinking	Being Numerate
I know myself better ☐ I made decisions ☐ I set goals ☐ I achieved goals ☐ I thought about what I learned ☐ I used technology to learn ☐	I am healthy and active ☐ I am social ☐ I am safe ☐ I feel confident ☐ I feel positive about what I learned ☐	I gathered and analysed information ☐ I thought creatively ☐ I thought about what I learned ☐ I used digital technology to access, manage and share information ☐	I estimated, predicted and calculated ☐ I was interested in problem-solving ☐

Being Creative	Working with Others	Communicating	Being Literate
I thought about things from a different point of view ☐ I put ideas into action ☐ I learned in a creative way ☐ I was creative with digital technology ☐	I developed relationships ☐ I dealt with conflict ☐ I cooperated ☐ I respected difference ☐ I learned with others ☐ I worked with others using digital technology ☐	I listened to my classmates ☐ I expressed myself ☐ I performed/presented ☐ I had a discussion/debate ☐ I used digital technology to communicate ☐	I understood some new words ☐ I wrote for different reasons ☐ I expressed my ideas clearly ☐ I developed my spoken language ☐ I read and wrote in different ways ☐

Discuss two skills (above) that you intend to focus on more in the future.

_____
_____
_____
_____

Athletics
Chapter 04

Introduction

The word 'athletics' comes from the Greek word *athlos*, which means contest. Athletics is a collection of different sporting events that utilises many FMS of running, jumping and throwing. There is a wide variety of events within each of these categories, including sprinting, middle distance, long distance and relay in running; long jump, triple jump, high jump and pole vault in jumping; and shot-put, hammer, discus and javelin in throwing.

The diverse nature of these athletics events provides many opportunities for everybody to be successful across a range of activities, regardless of pre-existing skills or knowledge. Participating in athletics and achieving a level of skill in any of the events will improve your performance in other sporting endeavours. The basic skills of running, jumping and throwing in athletics are easily transferrable to other sporting and recreational activities.

Common terms

Track events	Events that occur on the running track: • Sprints (100 m, 200 m, 400 m) • Middle distance (800 m, 1,500 m) • Long distance (3,000 m, 5,000 m and 10,000 m) • Relay (4 × 100 m and 4 × 400 m)	
Field events	Events that occur off the track: • High jump • Long jump • Triple jump • Pole vault • Hammer • Discus • Javelin • Shot-put	
Multisport events	**Heptathlon** Seven events, female only: • 100 m hurdles • High jump • Shot-put • 200 m • Long jump • Javelin • 800 m	**Decathlon** 10 events, male only: • 100 m • 110 m hurdles • High jump • Shot-put • 400 m • Long jump • Javelin • Discus • Pole vault • 1,500 m
Hurdles	Event where athletes jump over barriers	
Approach	Run-up phase during jumping events	
Baton	Hollow tube passed between runners in relay event	
Endurance	Being able to perform an activity for an extended time	
Technique	The most skilful way of performing an activity	
Horizontal	Parallel to the ground	
Vertical	Perpendicular to the ground	

1. Sprint start

Sprinting is one of the most popular events in athletics. Male and female athletes compete in these events, over different distances including: 60 m (indoor only), 100 m, 200 m and 400 m. Each event takes place on a 400 m track. The current world record for the male 100 m was set by Usain Bolt in 2009 and is 9.58 seconds. In 1988, Florence Griffith-Joyner set the world record for the female 100 m, and the record remains unbroken at 10.49 seconds. Because of the quick speed of these events, the **sprint start** is very important to successful performance.

Task 1

Unscramble these anagrams of common athletics terms.

Sign print		**Queen Itch**	
Tarts		**Deeps**	
Doc Err		**Rep Ow**	
Poison it		**Infests**	

Task 2

For this task, you will practise and perform the sprint start.
To assess your partner's technique:

* Ask your partner to begin with the starting position and to run for at least 20 m to achieve full speed.

* Ensure there is adequate space for acceleration and deceleration.

* Watch your partner from the side and from the front, to get a full view of their technique.

* Watch your partner at least once for each technical point.

Choose a partner to work with

1. Ask your partner to assess your technique and to tick 'Mastered', 'Nearly there' or 'Needs more practice'.
2. Answer the questions below.

	Correct technique			
On your marks ...	Is the front foot positioned behind the start line?	○	○	○
	Is the knee of the back leg beside the front foot?	○	○	○
	Are the hands wider than shoulder-width apart? Do the hands form a V-shape between the thumb and fingers? Are the hands placed along the start line, thumbs facing each other?	○	○	○
	Are the shoulders above the start line, with the head, neck and back in a straight line?	○	○	○
Set position ...	Are the hips raised slightly above the shoulders?	○	○	○
	Does the front knee have a 90-degree bend? Is the back leg slightly bent?	○	○	○
	Are the shoulders above the start line?	○	○	○
Go!	Does the sprinter push hard into the ground, straightening the front leg?	○	○	○
	Does the sprinter quickly pull the back knee up and forwards?	○	○	○
	Does the sprinter keep the body leaning forwards (does not straighten up)?	○	○	○

1. List one element from each phase that your partner did well:

   On your marks: _____

   Set position: _____

   Go: _____

2. List one element from each phase that your partner can improve:

   On your marks: _____

   Set position: _____

   Go: _____

Task 3

Try sprinting from (a) crouched position and from (b) standing position.

1. Which did you find easier to do? Why?

   _____

   _____

2. Which did you find faster? Why?

   _____

   _____

3. Choose one part of this technique and describe why it is important to good sprint starts:

    _____

    _____

4. List some advantages and disadvantages of using starting blocks.

    _____

    _____

5. Being a good sprinter would be useful for other sports too. Name two of these sports and explain why.

    _____

    _____

FMS

Why not take this opportunity to work with a partner to assess your running technique? Go to pp.4–5 and follow the instructions.

2. Shot-put

Shot-put is one of the throwing events in track and field athletics. It is believed to have originated in the Middle Ages, when soldiers would compete to see who could throw a cannonball the furthest.

In shot-put events today, men and women throw a heavy ball from inside a circle. The throw distance is measured from the edge of the circle to the nearest mark made by the shot-put when it first lands. Current world records are 23.12 m for men and 22.63 m for women.

Task

For this task, you will practise and perform the shot-put. To assess your partner's technique:

- Watch your partner from the side and from the front, to get a full view of their technique.
- Watch your partner at least once for each technical point.

Choose a partner to work with

1. Ask your partner to assess your technique and to tick 'Mastered', 'Nearly there' or 'Needs more practice'.
2. Answer the questions on p.145.

	Correct technique	⬤	◯	⬤
Before the throw	Is the ball touching the neck?	◯	◯	◯
	Are the shoulders facing away from the throwing direction?	◯	◯	◯
	Is the athlete looking down?	◯	◯	◯
	Is their weight on the back foot?	◯	◯	◯
	Is their throwing elbow high?	◯	◯	◯
During the throw	Does the ball stay touching the neck?	◯	◯	◯
	Do the hips drive forwards and upwards?	◯	◯	◯
	Does the weight transfer from the back foot to the front foot?	◯	◯	◯
After the throw	Does the arm straighten and push high?	◯	◯	◯
	Do the legs fully extend?	◯	◯	◯

1. What did your partner do well?

    _____

    _____

    _____

2. How can your partner improve?

    _____

    _____

    _____

3. I think my own shot-put throw can get better if I:

    _____

    _____

    _____

4. In your opinion, what are the top three technical points for a good shot-put throw?

    (a) _____

    (b) _____

    (c) _____

5. Angles are important in this sport. Why is this the case?

    _____

6. In the space below, design a game or activity that would help beginners to improve their technique.

7. The women's world record shot-put is greater than the men's record: 23.63 m versus 23.12 m. Can you think of any reason why this is the case?

    _____

    _____

    _____

    _____

3. Long jump

Long jump is one of the jumping events in track and field athletics. It is a jump for distance that is measured horizontally (similar to the triple jump). The high jump and pole vault are jumps for height and are measured vertically. The long jump was thought to be one of the most difficult events of the ancient Olympic Games. The long jump requires speed, strength, agility and flexibility.

Today's male athletes can jump almost 9 m: the World Record (WR) is 8.95 m. Female athletes can jump over 7.5 metres: WR 7.52 m. The jump is measured from the take-off board to the nearest mark in the landing area.

Task

Choose a partner to work with

1. Ask your partner to assess your technique and to tick 'Mastered', 'Nearly there' or 'Needs more practice'.

2. Answer the questions on p.147.

	Correct technique			
Run-up	Does the athlete run fast, all the way to the take-off board?	○	○	○
Take-off	Do they take off with one foot on the board?	○	○	○
	Do they jump at a 45-degree angle?	○	○	○
Flight	Do they use the arms for balance and height?	○	○	○
	Do they swing the legs forward for extra momentum?	○	○	○
Landing	Do they land two-footed in the sand?	○	○	○
	Are the arms and head leaning forward on landing?	○	○	○

1. What did your partner do well?

2. Choose one area where your partner can improve.

3. Give your partner some advice to help them improve in this area.

4. I think I could jump further if I:

5. In the table below, describe the actions of the body parts during the different phases of the long jump.

	Run-up	Take-off/Flight	Landing
Arms			
Legs			
Torso			

FMS The long jump is a sport-specific development of jumping for distance. Go to pp.18–19, follow the instructions and assess your jumping technique.

4. Relay baton exchange

Relay racing is similar to sprinting, and it involves four people running as part of a team. Each person runs a different section of the race while carrying a baton, and the baton is then handed over to the next person on their team. The winning team is the team that gets the baton over the end line in the shortest time. There are two types of relay races, the 4 × 100 m and 4 × 400 m (respectively, each athlete runs 100 m or 400 m before handing the baton to the next runner).

The handover of the baton is one of the most important aspects of relay racing. The handover must be done at high speed, within a 20 m changeover zone. Although several different methods are allowed for handing over the baton, the *push technique* is the method used by USA teams and Jamaica teams (the teams that dominate this race). The current world records for the 4 × 100 m are 36.84 seconds for men (set by Jamaica in 2012) and 40.82 seconds for women (set by the USA in 2012).

Task

For this task, you will work in a group of four: two pairs of partners.
- Choose one person to be the first runner, and another person to be the second runner.
- The other two group members will assess the runners.
- Mark out a 20 m area on your 'track', where the baton exchange takes place.
- The two runners take turns in exchanging the baton.
- The other two group members complete the table on p.149.

1. In your opinion, why is the baton held at the bottom by the first runner?

   _____

   _____

2. Why is it important that the second runner gets the baton at full speed?

   _____

   _____

3. Do you think the four changeovers in a 4 × 400 m relay would be different? How and why?

   _____

   _____

   _____

   _____

   _____

   _____

   _____

   _____

4. In a 4 × 100 m relay:

- Athlete A runs in 11.03 seconds
- Athlete B runs in 10.55 seconds
- Athlete C runs in 10.38 seconds
- Athlete D runs in 10.45 seconds

(a) What was their finish time?

_____

(b) Calculate the average speed over the race.

_____

(c) On average, how fast are they running in km/h?

_____

(d) What finish time would runner A have if they could maintain their average speed over a 5,000 m race?

_____

(e) Can you suggest some ways for the team to improve their time?

_____

_____

	Correct technique	○	○	○
First runner	Is the baton held in the right hand, near the bottom of the baton?	○	○	○
	Does the runner run along the left side of the lane?	○	○	○
	Does the runner hold the baton vertically and place it accurately into the hand of the second runner?	○	○	○
Second runner	Does the starting position allow a good view of the first runner as they approach?	○	○	○
	Does the starting position allow for a fast sprint start?	○	○	○
	Is the left hand extended directly behind the runner? Is the hand open, with the thumb facing the ground?	○	○	○
Timing	Does the handover happen within the 20 m handover zone?	○	○	○
	Is the second runner at full speed when receiving the baton?	○	○	○
	Do both runners stay within their running lanes?	○	○	○

5. Javelin

Javelin is a stand-alone discipline, and is also part of the decathlon and heptathlon events. Male athletes can throw almost 100 m (WR 98.48 m). Female athletes can throw over 70 m (WR 72.28 m). The current Irish junior records are 67.22 m and 47.52 m for boys and girls respectively.

Task

1. What is a javelin?
   (a) A disc-like object made of fibreglass and rubber
   (b) A spear-like object made of rubber
   (c) A disc-like object made of metal
   (d) A spear-like object made of metal and fibreglass

2. How do you win a javelin event?

3. How is a javelin throw measured?
   (a) From the backline of the run-up to where the javelin stops moving
   (b) From the frontline of the run-up to where the javelin stops moving
   (c) From the frontline of the run-up to where the javelin first lands
   (d) From the backline of the run-up to where the javelin first lands

4. Which one of the following aspects is part of a valid javelin throw?
   (a) The javelin should travel horizontally.
   (b) The point of the javelin must touch the ground first.
   (c) The tail of the javelin must touch the ground first.
   (d) The javelin must spin during flight.

5. What is considered a foul in javelin?

6. Ideally, at what angle should the javelin be released?
   (a) 45 degrees
   (b) 90 degrees
   (c) Less than 45 degrees
   (d) More than 90 degrees

7. In your opinion, why is this the case?

6. Triple jump

The triple jump is sometimes referred to as the 'hop, skip and jump'. It is similar to the long jump. The athlete must travel as far as possible in a horizontal direction by running down a take-off track and then performing a hop, skip and jump into a sandpit. The first hop must begin before the take-off board on the track. The jump is measured from the take-off board to the closest mark made by the athlete in the sandpit. The current world records are 18.29 m for a male athlete, and 15.50 m for a female athlete.

Task 1

Choose a partner to work with

1. Ask your partner to assess your technique and to tick 'Mastered', 'Nearly there' or 'Needs more practice'.
2. Answer the questions on p.152.

	Correct technique			
Run	Is top running speed maintained before the hop?	○	○	○
	Does the hop begin at the take-off board?	○	○	○
Hop	Does the hop start on one foot and land on the same foot?	○	○	○
	Are the arms bent at 90 degrees? Does the athlete drive the opposite arm to leg, for balance?	○	○	○
Skip	Does the athlete jump from one foot to the other?	○	○	○
	Is the arm drive used to increase distance and maintain balance?	○	○	○
Jump	Does the jump begin from one foot? Are both feet together on landing?	○	○	○
	Do the arms swing up and forwards, to increase height and momentum?	○	○	○
	Do the arms swing back at the end, to gain maximum distance?	○	○	○

1. Why is it important to be running at full speed before the hop?

2. Which phase did you find most difficult? Why?

3. What other activities could you practise to improve your triple jump performance?

Task 2

The table below shows the winning distances for the Men's Triple Jump Olympic Competitions since 1984.

Year	1984	1988	1992	1996	2000	2004	2008	2012	2016	2020
Result (m)	17.26	17.61	18.17	19.09	17.71	17.79	17.67	17.81	17.86	

(a) Use the axis below to chart the results.

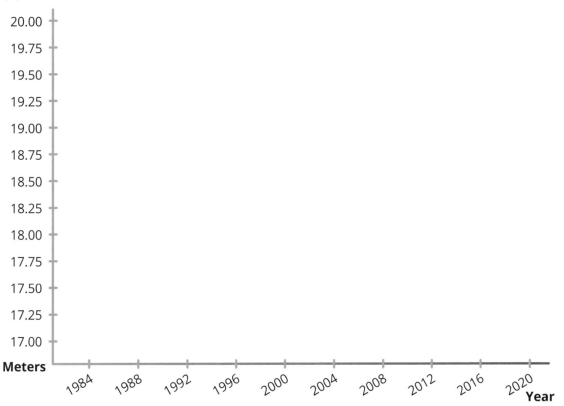

(b) Are there any trends or anomalies (unusual results) in your graph?

_____

_____

_____

(c) Calculate the average distance jumped since 1984.

_____

(d) What is the difference in metres between the shortest and the longest jump?

_____

(e) Can you think of any reasons for this difference?

_____

(f) Can you predict the result for 2020?

_____

7. High jump

High jump is one of the vertically measured jumping events. Today's athletes use the Fosbury Flop method: jumping head first, backwards over the bar. Before this method became popular, athletes would straddle jump, roll or scissors over the bar.

High jump athletes tend to be tall and lean. Elite male athletes can jump almost 2.5 metres (WR 2.45 m). Female athletes can jump over 2 m (WR 2.09 m). Athletes land on deep padded mats to prevent injury.

Task 1

1. What physical attributes might help high jumpers to be successful?

2. Before you begin practising this activity, estimate who in your class will be the best at high jump. Predict the top three jumpers in your group.

3. Why do you think they will be good?

4. Take a quick survey of all the sports played by your classmates.
   (a) Is there a link between any particular sports and high jump ability?
   (b) Can you explain this link?

Task 2

For this task, you will practise and perform the high jump.
To assess your partner's technique:

- Record your partner from the side and from the front, to get a full view of their technique.

- Watch your partner at least once for each technical point.

Choose a partner to work with

1. Ask your partner to assess your technique and to tick 'Mastered', 'Nearly there' or 'Needs more practice'.

2. Answer the questions on p.156.

Note: Coach's Eye is a useful video analysis app for this task.

Scissors	Correct technique	●	○	●
Run-up	Does the athlete approach the bar at an angle?	○	○	○
Take-off	Are the arms reaching upwards?	○	○	○
	Does the leg closest to the bar drive up first?	○	○	○
Flight	Does the athlete whip the other leg over quickly?	○	○	○
Landing	Does the athlete land on their feet?	○	○	○

Flop	Correct technique	●	○	●
Run-up	Does the athlete approach the bar at an angle?	○	○	○
Take-off	Are the arms reaching (bar side) up and over the bar?	○	○	○
	Does the leg closest to the bar drive up first?	○	○	○
	Does the athlete rotate the hips, putting their back to the bar?	○	○	○
Flight	Does the athlete arch the back and bring the legs together?	○	○	○
	Does the athlete bend the knees and lift the feet over the bar?	○	○	○
Landing	Does the athlete tuck their chin and land on their back?	○	○	○

1. Work with your partner to discuss these questions, and note any interesting points:

   (a) In your opinion, which technique suits you best?

   _____

   (b) What is your partner's opinion on this? Do you both agree?

   _____

   _____

   (c) Which technique gave you your highest jump?

   _____

2. Choose one area of your jump where you and your partner think you can improve.

   _____

   _____

3. How can you do this?

   _____

   _____

   _____

4. Name a sport where being a good high jumper could be useful. Why do you think this is?

   _____

8. Discus

The discus is a track and field event that dates to ancient Greece. It involves throwing a disc-shaped object as far as possible. The size and weight of the discus is different for men, women and children. All female athletes and male athletes under 14 years of age use a 1 kg discus. The weight increases to 2 kg for adult male athletes only. The thrower stands in a circle 2.5 m in diameter and throws the discus as far as possible, while staying within the circle. To improve the throw, athletes will often spin around in the circle to create power and speed before throwing the discus. This can result in very long throws. The current world records are 74.08 m for a male athlete, and 76.80 m for a female athlete.

Task

Research how to perform the discus throw correctly. Use this information to design a checklist of the main technical points of the discus throw. Complete the template below.

Phase	Correct technique			
		○	○	○
		○	○	○
		○	○	○
		○	○	○
		○	○	○
		○	○	○
		○	○	○

1. List four key safety issues that must be considered when throwing the discus.

   _____

   _____

2. In your opinion, which phase of the throw is the most important? Explain.

   _____

   _____

3. Discus throwers typically look different from high jumpers. Why?

   _____

9. Racewalk

This event is notorious for its unusual body movements. While it might look different from other sports, it is very demanding. Unlike runners, racewalkers must keep at least one foot in contact with the ground at all times, and their front leg must always be straight. These rules combine to give racewalking its famous side-to-side hip action.

The Olympic distances for racewalkers are 20 km and 50 km. To put that into context, the M50 motorway in Dublin is only 45 km long! The fastest walkers in the world move at speeds of around 13 km/h.

> **Remember**: one stride is counted from when your right foot leaves the ground until it strikes the ground again.

Task

For this task, work with your partner to practise racewalking. You will need a timer and a measuring tape.

1. How fast can you walk 100 m?

2. How fast can you walk 400 m?

3. How many strides does it take you to walk 100 m?

4. Measure your stride length.

5. How many strides should it take you to walk 400 m (based on your stride length)?

6. Walk 400 m while counting your strides. Did the numbers match? Why/why not?

10. Distance running

Distance running is divided into middle distances and long distances. Middle distance races are 800 m and 1,500 m. Long distance is anything over 3,000 m. This includes the steeplechase (with obstacles), 5,000 m race, 10,000 m race, and marathon (42.2 km).

Tactics are important in all races. Athletics experts argue that tactics become even more significant over the longer distances. Athletes need to consider many different factors, including pacing, feeding, gait and fatigue.

Task 1

In this task, you will work with a partner to learn about pacing in races.

* Choose a distance you are comfortable with. Divide it into laps or sections.

* Work with your partner to set a suitable target time for the completing the entire race.

* Divide the target time for the entire race by the number of laps or sections. This will give you lap/section target times.

* As you run the race, your partner will compare your speed for each lap/section to the target time for each lap/section. This allows you to adjust your speed and pace yourself to finish the distance as close to the target time as possible.

Task 2

Repeat Task 1 without your partner. Keep your own time and adjust your pace yourself.

Task 3

For this task, choose your distance (middle or long). Estimate your time to complete it. This is a race against yourself!

Race distance	
Estimated finish time	
Actual finish time	

1. Was your time accurate?

   _____

2. If your time was not accurate, can you explain why?

   _____

   _____

3. What could you do to improve your accuracy?

   _____

   _____

   _____

Task 4

Research the current world record holders for the distances below. Record their times and calculate their speeds. Answer the questions below.

	Fastest male athlete		Fastest female athlete	
	Time	Speed	Time	Speed
100 m				
400 m				
5,000 m				
10,000 m				
Marathon				

1. Calculate the average speed of each athlete.

2. Compare the speeds over the different distances. Identify any trends. Discuss your findings with your partner.

End-of-unit assessment 1: Individual event

Attending an athletics event or watching one on TV gives you an idea of how good the best athletes in the world are compared to each other. However, you do not really get a feel for just how skilled these performers are until you try a skill yourself! In this task, you have the chance to pit your abilities against the best in the world.

Read through this classroom-based assessment in full before you begin.

My athlete's profile

Choose a famous athlete.

- Write a brief profile of the athlete. Include the details below.

> **Note**: Before you write a profile for your athlete, ensure you can find enough information about them online. Many athletes post information about themselves and their training online.

Photo

_____

- Height:
- Birthplace:

- Weight:
- Lives:

- Date of birth:
- Event:

- World records or career highlights:

- Elements of training programme:

My athlete's technique

- Find footage of your profiled athlete performing in their event. Write tips that would help a beginner to master the techniques shown by your chosen athlete.

Tips for good technique

My technique

Record a video of yourself performing the same event/skill as the athlete. Complete the self-assessment wheel to assess your ability in this skill.

> **Note**: See p.24 for more information on self-assessment wheels.

1. Fill in a short description for each of the technical points.

2. Fill in your current skill level. For each of the technical points, award yourself a score between 1 and 4. For example, a score of 1 means: 'I cannot do this.' If you score 1, shade one segment of the wheel. If you score 2, shade two segments.

3. When you have assessed each technical point, zoom out and look at the entire wheel. It will be clear to see which technical points are mastered, and which can be improved.

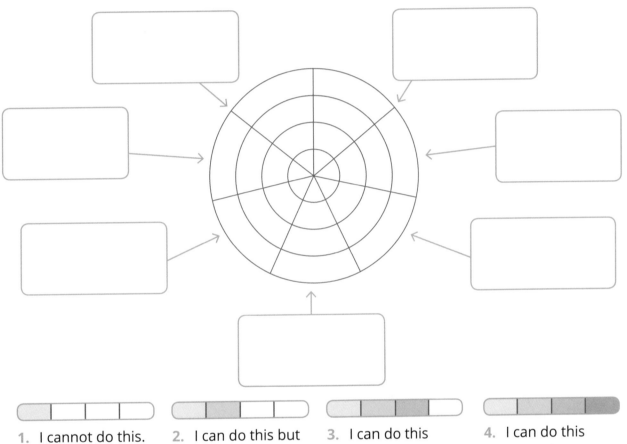

1. I cannot do this.
2. I can do this but I find it difficult.
3. I can do this most of the time.
4. I can do this every time.

My plan for improvement

Briefly describe some activities that could help you to improve your performance of this skill.

End-of-unit assessment 2: Mini-Olympics

Organising a mini-Olympic event will encourage you to use many of the Key Skills you have learned in Junior Cycle PE, including Communication, Literacy, Numeracy, Creativity and Working with Others. You will work as part of a team, making decisions through discussion and compromise. Then you will analyse these decisions and reflect on the assessment.

Instructions

- You will work in a small group to plan, run and evaluate a mini-Olympics event with six activities.

- Use the template on p.165 to plan all aspects of the event.

- Decide which activities to include. (This will depend on the equipment and space available.)

- Identify all the equipment needed for each activity.

- Draw a map of the competition area and decide how and where to set up each event.

- Include a timetable for the mini-Olympics, which allows the whole class to compete in all the events. Remember: your timetable needs to include enough time for set-up, warm-up, competing, judging and announcing the winners.

- When all plans are complete, each group presents their plan to the class. Your class will analyse each proposal and vote to select the best one.

- You will then participate in the chosen mini-Olympics.

- Afterwards, each group will write two reflections:

  - In Reflection 1 (p.166), your group will analyse and evaluate your original mini-Olympics proposal to identify areas that could be improved.

  - In Reflection 2 (p.166), your group will analyse and evaluate the mini-Olympics you participated in. You will describe what went well and identify what improvements could be made, if the event was to be held again.

Activities for our mini-Olympics

1 _____
2 _____
3 _____
4 _____
5 _____
6 _____

Map for our mini-Olympics

Event planning for our mini-Olympics

Event	Equipment	Timing and safety

Reflection 1

Strengths of our proposal

Things that could be improved in our proposal

Reflection 2

What went well?

What could be improved? How?

Strand review
In this chapter, you learned about:

- Activities in track and field athletics ☐
- Developing the FMS of running, jumping and throwing ☐
- The most effective technique for performing each of the specific events in athletics ☐
- Analysing each athletics technique, using checklists ☐
- Assessing your own ability to perform a skill, using video footage ☐
- Using technology to record a partner performing a skill ☐

- Assessing a partner's ability to perform a skill, using technical points ☐
- Providing feedback to a partner and discussing what is (or is not) correct technique ☐
- Analysing a skill and identifying the key characteristics necessary for success ☐
- Cooperation, communication and teamwork, and why they are important for group work ☐
- Contributing in a positive manner as part of group ☐

Look back over the activities you completed. Tick the skills you used.

Managing Myself	Staying Well	Managing Information and Thinking	Being Numerate
I know myself better ☐	I am healthy and active ☐	I gathered and analysed information ☐	I estimated, predicted and calculated ☐
I made decisions ☐	I am social ☐	I thought creatively ☐	I was interested in problem-solving ☐
I set goals ☐	I am safe ☐	I thought about what I learned ☐	
I achieved goals ☐	I feel confident ☐	I used digital technology to access, manage and share information ☐	
I thought about what I learned ☐	I feel positive about what I learned ☐		
I used technology to learn ☐			

Being Creative	Working with Others	Communicating	Being Literate
I thought about things from a different point of view ☐	I developed relationships ☐	I listened to my classmates ☐	I understood some new words ☐
I put ideas into action ☐	I dealt with conflict ☐	I expressed myself ☐	I wrote for different reasons ☐
I learned in a creative way ☐	I cooperated ☐	I performed/presented ☐	I expressed my ideas clearly ☐
I was creative with digital technology ☐	I respected difference ☐	I had a discussion/debate ☐	I developed my spoken language ☐
	I learned with others ☐	I used digital technology to communicate ☐	I read and wrote in different ways ☐
	I worked with others using digital technology ☐		

Discuss two skills (above) that you intend to focus on more in the future.

_____

_____

_____

_____

Aquatics
Chapter 05

Introduction

Aquatics is an important area of the PE curriculum. It is very different from the other areas, in that it generally takes place in a swimming pool – not in a sports hall! Some of you may have learned to swim at a young age; some of you may not know how to swim yet. But aquatics is for everyone, regardless of whether you can swim or not.

Swimming, and moving in the water generally, can be really enjoyable activities. Aquatics gives you the opportunity to learn about and do body movements that aren't possible in any other environment.

In this chapter you will learn about water safety – how to be safe in and around the water. You will learn how to keep yourself afloat until someone can come to help you, and how to help someone if you see them in difficulty in the water. You will also see how the components of fitness, which we learned about in Chapter 2, are just as relevant to water movements as they are to movements on land! And finally, yes – you will also learn a little about swimming strokes! Whether you are a beginner or have been swimming for years, you can always improve your technique.

Common terms

Aquatics	An area of the PE curriculum which is about moving in and around the water
Physical fitness	A combination of how well your heart and lungs can keep working at a hard intensity; how strong your muscles are and how long they can keep working for; your flexibility; and your body composition
Improvement plan	A plan designed to practise, monitor and develop a skill or ability over time
Goal	The intention or target you aim to achieve in your plan

1. Aqua fitness profile

In aquatics, there are two components of fitness we can focus on particularly well: cardiovascular endurance (CVE) and local muscular endurance (LME). A circuit is a type of fitness session that lets us move from one activity to another, in a series.

Task

Remember: your aqua fitness scores are just about you. It makes no sense to compare your scores with anyone else's scores. Just compare your scores *now* with the scores you get in the *future*, as you track your fitness.

For each activity in the circuit, record how many times you did the exercise within the given timeframe (i.e. how many repetitions or 'reps'). Complete the table below. Make sure that you use the same time frame (e.g. 1 minute or 2 minutes) each time you do the test so that you can compare your results.

	Test 1 Date:	Test 2 Date:
CVE 1: Jumping Jacks		
LME 1: Frontal kickboard push down (arms)		
CVE 2: Side slides, across pool		
LME 2: Squat jumps		
CVE 3: Lateral jumps		
LME 3: Sidebar press-ups		

Reflection: Test 1 and personal improvement plan

1. Which component(s) of fitness would you like to improve? Why?

   _____

   _____

   _____

2. Write a personal improvement plan for how you will progress in the next
   six weeks.

   _____

   _____

   _____

   _____

   _____

   _____

   _____

   _____

   _____

   _____

   _____

   _____

   _____

   _____

   _____

   _____

   _____

Reflection: Test 2

1. Did you maintain or improve CVE and LME fitness?

   _____

2. Why was this the case?

   _____

   _____

   _____

3. What is your next target for aqua fitness, and how will you achieve it?

   _____

   _____

   _____

2. Elementary backstroke

The elementary backstroke is a nice, easy stroke to use to keep you afloat in the water, to travel across the water, and to conserve energy! It is great to learn this stroke before progressing to the more formal backstroke that we see swimmers use in competitions.

For this task, your partner will assess you as you complete the elementary backstroke, at least twice across the pool. For each of the criteria below, your partner will identify whether you are developing, achieving or excelling.

Task

Choose a partner to work with

1. Ask your partner to assess your technique and to tick 'Mastered', 'Nearly there' or 'Needs more practice'.
2. Then work with your partner to answer the questions on p.173.

Does the swimmer slide the fingers up along the sides as the elbows bend – like a monkey scratching under the armpits?	○	○	○
Does the swimmer extend the arms and fingers out to make a letter T?	○	○	○
Do they push water towards the feet, using the palms of the hands?	○	○	○
Do they frog-kick at the same time that they push with the hands?	○	○	○
Do they finish with the body relaxed, legs straight, and arms at the side of the body, for a glide?	○	○	○

Monkey scratching under armpits

Stretch arms out to make T and pull knees up

Push down with arms and frog kick at same time

Finish with arms by side and legs straight for a glide

Ask your partner to complete Questions 1 and 2. Then answer Questions 3 and 4 for yourself.

1. My partner is doing really well at:

2. My partner can improve by:

3. Did you agree with the feedback your partner gave you on your technique? (Yes/No. Explain.)

4. How did you feel when your partner gave you feedback on your elementary backstroke technique?

3. Front crawl

The front crawl is often considered the fastest of all the swimming strokes. It is the quickest way to get from one end of the pool to the other ... once you've mastered it! This assessment will help you and your partner to improve your front crawl technique. You will need to work together – you will give your partner feedback, and they will give you feedback.

For this task, your partner will assess you as you complete the front crawl, at least twice across the pool. For each of the criteria below, your partner will identify whether you are developing, achieving or excelling.

Task

Choose a partner to work with

1. Ask your partner to assess your technique and to tick 'Mastered', 'Nearly there' or 'Needs more practice'.
2. Then work with your partner to answer the questions on p.175.

Is the swimmer's body flat in the water, parallel to the surface, during the stroke?	◯	◯	◯
Does the swimmer initiate the kick from their hips and have 'floppy' ankles?	◯	◯	◯
Does the swimmer keep a high elbow during the 'recovery' phase?	◯	◯	◯
Does the swimmer reach far as the arm enters the water for the 'pull' phase?	◯	◯	◯
Does the swimmer keep the head in the water, and rotate it to breathe to the side?	◯	◯	◯

Pull phase	**Recovery phase**
Body flat in water	Elbow kept high in recovery phase
Head stays in water	Keep head in water and rotate to side to breathe Kick comes from hips, 'floppy' ankles
Reach far as pull phase starts	

Ask your partner to complete Questions 1 and 2. Then answer Questions 3 and 4 for yourself.

1. My partner is doing really well at:

   _____

   _____

   _____

2. My partner can improve by:

   _____

   _____

   _____

   _____

   _____

   _____

   _____

3. Did you agree with the feedback your partner gave you on your technique? (Yes/No. Explain.)

   _____

   _____

   _____

   _____

   _____

4. How did you feel when your partner gave you feedback on your front crawl technique?

   _____

   _____

   _____

   _____

   _____

4. Breaststroke

In the breaststroke, the arms and legs work at different times: first you **pull** with the arms, then you **breathe**, then you **kick** with the legs, and then you **glide!** In this assessment, we will look at the basic movement of coordinating the arms and legs: pull, breathe, kick and glide.

For this task, your partner will assess you as you complete the breaststroke, at least twice across the pool. For each of the criteria below, your partner will identify whether you are developing, achieving, or excelling. Because there are so many parts to this stroke, it can be tricky to analyse performance. A good tip is to focus on just one phase (e.g. the pull) at a time.

Task

Choose a partner to work with

1. Ask your partner to assess your technique and to tick 'Mastered', 'Nearly there' or 'Needs more practice'.
2. Then work with your partner to answer the questions on p.177.

Pull			
Does the swimmer pull the arms in a semicircular movement towards the body?	○	○	○
Does the swimmer keep the legs straight behind?	○	○	○
Breathe			
Does the swimmer pull the arms in under the chest and lift the chin to take a breath?	○	○	○
Does the swimmer tuck in the legs and turn out the heels?	○	○	○
Kick			
Does the swimmer straighten out the arms?	○	○	○
Does the swimmer whip the legs back in a semicircle with a 'snap' motion (frog kick)?	○	○	○

Glide

Does the swimmer glide through the water with arms and legs outstretched (streamlined) for a second or two (not kicking or pulling)?

Ask your partner to complete Questions 1 and 2. Then answer Questions 3 and 4 for yourself.

1. My partner is doing really well at:

   _____

   _____

2. My partner can improve by:

   _____

   _____

3. Did you agree with the feedback your partner gave you on your technique? (Yes/No. Explain.)

   _____

   _____

   _____

4. How did you feel when your partner gave you feedback on your breaststroke technique?

   _____

   _____

   _____

Pull	**Breathe**	**Kick**	**Glide**
Arms reach forward and pull in semicircle towards body	Pull arms in under chest, and lift chin to breathe Tuck in legs and turn out heels	Straighten out arms Whip legs back in semicircle – frog kick	Straighten arms and legs fully and glide

5. Water safety and the community

There are many places in the local community where we need to be conscious of water safety. This could include local rivers and lakes, swimming pools and the sea (if you live by the coast). This could even include a slurry pit, if you live near or on a farm. We all need to take responsibility for water safety in any way we can. For example: if you notice that a ring buoy is damaged, inform the local Gardaí.

Task

- This assessment is a homework assignment that you will complete **with a parent or guardian**. Together with this responsible adult, you will carry out an inventory of the potential water hazards in your local area (i.e. your town or community).

- You will identify each potential water hazard (e.g. river, lake or swimming pool).

- For each potential hazard, you will assess the safety equipment nearby.

- Write a recommendation for how the area could be improved to make it safer (e.g. install a ring buoy, display a warning sign or erect a barrier).

Name of local area:		
Potential water hazard	**Safety equipment nearby**	**Recommendation**
1		
2		
3		
4		

6. Cold water!

We need to be very careful beside water: we always need to respect it. Even if you can swim well, the shock of falling into cold water can cause the best swimmer to get into trouble!

Task

If you ever fall into cold water, there are four **life-saving steps** you can take. The table below shows pictures of these life-saving steps. For each picture, identify what the swimmer is doing, and write a description for this life-saving step.

Image	Description

7. What I know about aquatics

Task

1. List three exercises you can do in the swimming pool to work on cardiovascular endurance.

    _____

    _____

2. List three exercises you can do in the swimming pool to work on local muscular endurance?

    _____

    _____

3. The pictures below show someone doing the front crawl.
    *   On the pictures, **circle** three parts of the body where this swimmer's technique is not quite right.

    *   **List** three things this swimmer could do to improve the quality of their stroke.

    (a) _____

    _____

    (b) _____

    _____

    (c) _____

    _____

possible CBA End-of-unit assessment: Water safety scenario

For this task:

- You will work with a partner to complete the scenario below.

- On Day 1, you will complete the scenario twice: once as the swimmer, and once as the rescuer.

- On Day 2, you will complete the scenario twice: once as the swimmer, and once as the rescuer.

- This way, both you and your partner can track your progress in each role (progress as swimmer and progress as rescuer).

Scenario

Swimmer

You are swimming in the pool. You duck-dive to retrieve an object from the bottom of the pool. You hold the object over your head with one hand, while treading water for 1 minute. You then realise you have hurt your arm, and cannot swim back to the side of the pool. You call for help. You tread water as you wait to be rescued.

Rescuer

You hear someone calling for help, and implement the four steps for a reach-pole rescue, to bring the swimmer to the side of the pool:

- Voice contact

- Call for help

- Correct lying body position

- Reach with the pole

Day 1

- Complete Self-Assessment Wheel 1 on p.183.
- Answer the questions below.
- Create your personal improvement plan.

---

1. Which part of the scenario did you find easiest to do? Why?

_____

_____

2. Which part of the scenario did you find most difficulty? Why?

_____

_____

Personal improvement plan

My goal

Identify what you hope to improve on for Day 2 (e.g. ability to tread water, entering the water or using the reach pole).

_____

_____

_____

My plan

Explain what you need to do differently to get better at this activity. What will you work on and practise before Day 2?

_____

_____

_____

_____

_____

_____

_____

_____

_____

_____

_____

Self-Assessment Wheel 1

Water movement and survival

Retrieve and hold objects.

Tread water.

Remain upright on water entry.

Duck-dive.

Keep correct body position at the side of the pool.

Reach the pole rescue.

Call for help.

Make voice contact.

Rescue

1. I cannot do this.
2. I can do this but I find it difficult.
3. I can do this most of the time.
4. I can do this every time.

Self-Assessment Wheel 2

Water movement and survival

Retrieve and hold objects.

Tread water.

Remain upright on water entry.

Duck-dive.

Keep correct body position at the side of the pool.

Reach the pole rescue.

Call for help.

Make voice contact.

Rescue

1. I cannot do this.
2. I can do this but I find it difficult.
3. I can do this most of the time.
4. I can do this every time.

Possible classroom-based assessments

Day 2

- Complete Self-assessment Wheel 2 on p.183.
- Answer the questions below.

1. In which part of the scenario did you most improve, compared with Day 1?

2. Do you feel that your personal improvement plan worked for you? Were you able to follow your plan over the last few weeks? Explain your answer.

3. How would you change your plan, if you were to do this assessment again? What would you do differently to practise between Day 1 and Day 2?

Strand review
In this chapter, you learned about:

- The four steps for a reach-pole water rescue ☐
- How to tread water ☐
- How to duck-dive ☐
- How to remain upright when entering the water ☐
- How to retrieve objects from the bottom of the pool ☐

- That muscular endurance and cardiovascular endurance are just as important in the swimming pool as they are in the sports hall ☐
- The main criteria for correct technique in the elementary backstroke, front crawl and breaststroke ☐

Look back over the activities you completed. Tick the skills you used.

Managing Myself	Staying Well	Managing Information and Thinking	Being Numerate
I know myself better ☐	I am healthy and active ☐	I gathered and analysed information ☐	I estimated, predicted and calculated ☐
I made decisions ☐	I am social ☐	I thought creatively ☐	I was interested in problem-solving ☐
I set goals ☐	I am safe ☐	I thought about what I learned ☐	
I achieved goals ☐	I feel confident ☐		
I thought about what I learned ☐	I feel positive about what I learned ☐	I used digital technology to access, manage and share information ☐	
I used technology to learn ☐			

Being Creative	Working with Others	Communicating	Being Literate
I thought about things from a different point of view ☐	I developed relationships ☐	I listened to my classmates ☐	I understood some new words ☐
I put ideas into action ☐	I dealt with conflict ☐	I expressed myself ☐	I wrote for different reasons ☐
I learned in a creative way ☐	I cooperated ☐	I performed/presented ☐	I expressed my ideas clearly ☐
I was creative with digital technology ☐	I respected difference ☐	I had a discussion/debate ☐	I developed my spoken language ☐
	I learned with others ☐	I used digital technology to communicate ☐	I read and wrote in different ways ☐
	I worked with others using digital technology ☐		

Discuss two skills (above) that you intend to focus on more in the future.

_____

_____

_____

_____

Adventure activities

Chapter 06

Introduction

Adventure activities provide you with the opportunity to develop personally, socially and physically in a safe environment. You will learn and be supported in building your competence and confidence, as well as leadership and responsibility. You will be encouraged to set goals for yourself and for small teams, and to reflect on your experience and the progress made. There is an adventure activity for everyone. And through experiencing activities such as orienteering or team challenges, you may develop an interest in other activities, such as rock climbing, hill walking, caving, snorkelling, surfing, sailing or kayaking.

You may be confronted with your own uncertainties and fears, where failure is possible. However, this learning journey will teach you to acknowledge this reality and also learn to be more resilient. Adventure activities allow you to grow, because you live through situations that ultimately work towards developing your potential – personally, socially and physically.

Common terms

Orienteering	Activity that requires your navigation skills alone or with your partner – from point to point, using a map
Team challenges	Activities that require you to cooperate and problem-solve in achieving a common goal with others
Thumbing	Placing your thumb next to your current location on the map, while running (to save time)
Hand rails	A feature on your map that is easy to follow and closely resembles the route you want to take to your next control
Control	A checkpoint on an orienteering course that you must visit to complete the course
Cooperation	Working together to achieve the same goals
Course	Courses are made up of a number of controls that you must visit in order
Cross-county orienteering	Every competitor must visit the same controls in the same order
Score orienteering	The area is dotted with a large number of control points worth different points; competitors must gather as many controls as possible within a given time
Line orienteering	No controls are marked on the map, only the route. At various points along this line there are hidden controls. The competitor will find a control only by following the line.

1. Full value contract (FVC)

This contract is an agreement developed and agreed to by all the students in your class, so that everyone can succeed in adventure activities. You will be asked to understand, sign and agree to these behaviour guidelines, so that everyone knows what is expected.

Task: Our full value contract

1. Work in a group of six with a large piece of paper and a set of value statements.
2. As a group, select your **top six** statements.
3. Agree as a group which one of the six statements is the most important of the values.
4. Nominate a spokesperson for your group. The spokesperson will justify your group's top value.

Use the hand below to record the value statements selected by your group:
* Write the most important value on the palm of the hand
* Write the other five values on the four fingers and thumb.

1. How do you think a full value contract will benefit your class?

2. Which of these statements do you think will be most difficult for the class to keep? Why? How could you overcome this?

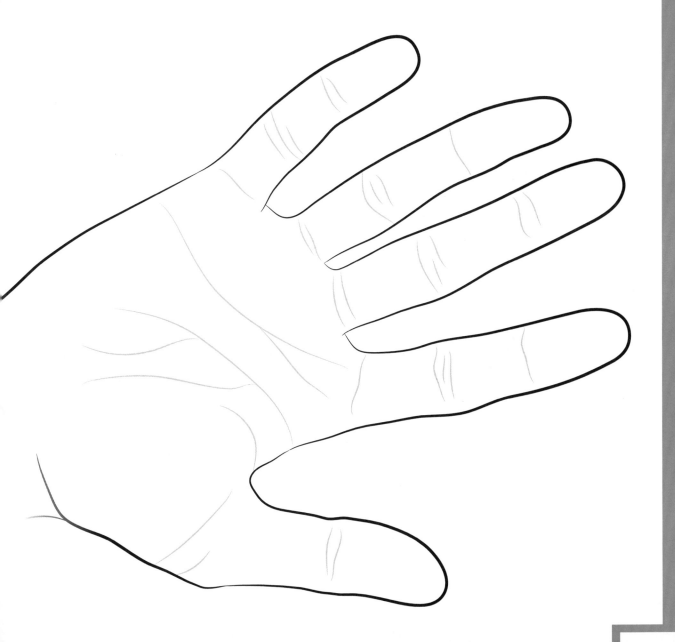

2. Map setting

Orienteering was first invented in Sweden in 1886 as a military exercise
that required soldiers to cross an unknown land, using only a map and
compass. Today orienteering is much the same: orienteering events will challenge
your map-reading skills and test your ability to get from one point to the next so that
you can collect controls using the map. In this task, you will use the map below to
navigate your way around cones laid out for you. When you are new to orienteering,
it is important that you try to work on correct technique, rather than speed.

Task 1: Navigating, using a map

You will work with a partner:

* Ensure you set your map to North by aligning the map in your hand with the
  direction of North identified by your teacher.

* Select which course to start with: A, B, C or D. You will take the lead on two of
  these courses; your partner will take the lead on the other two courses.

* Begin at the triangle. ▷ When you get to a designated cone, lift it and record the
  symbol shown underneath on your control card.

* Follow the line on the map and repeat the procedure for each cone, until you
  reach the finish point (the double circle). ◎

* When you have finished courses A–D, your teacher will provide you with the
  correct answers.

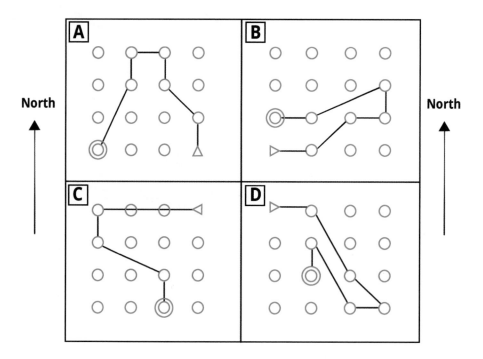

Task 2: Recording the controls

Symbols	1	2	3	4	5	6	7	Control card
Name:								
Partner's name:								
Course A								Score /7
Course B								Score /7
Course C								Score /7
Course D								Score /7
Total score								Score /28

Task 3: Identifying the symbols

1. You recorded 16 different symbols today. Can you identify what any of these symbols represent on an orienteering map? A bonus mark will be awarded for each correct symbol.

Record your answers here:

_____   _____   _____   _____

_____   _____   _____   _____

_____   _____   _____   _____

_____   _____   _____   _____

Score   / 16

Total score: Orienteering event + Identifying symbols: **/44**

Task 4: How did it go?

Answer the questions below to reflect on the overall success of today's tasks.

1. Did you learn any new skills today? Explain.

_____

_____

_____

_____

_____

2. Do you think these skills could be useful beyond PE class? How?

_____

_____

_____

3. Am I orienteering properly?

You are probably very familiar with your school grounds, and so you do not need to orienteer day to day. However, there are times when you will need to find your way in an area you do not know very well. This is when orienteering is useful. Being able to navigate towards your next destination (attack point) is an extremely useful orienteering skill.

Task

- You will work with a partner.

- Before you set off on your course, mark three spots on your route where you can take a time-out.

- When you take a time-out, you will use the table on p.193 to reflect on your technique.

- Remember that much of the enjoyment and learning is in the *doing* of the orienteering course – it is not just about the result!

- With your partner, decide who will ask the questions at each time-out, and who will fill in the table.

1. Can you and your partner successfully complete each reflection below? Circle Yes/No.

	1st reflection	2nd refection	3rd reflection
(a) *Is your map orientated?* Check and adjust as needed. Your thumb should be able to reach the centre of the map from all four sides of the map.	Yes/No	Yes/No	Yes/No
(b) *Where are you on the map?* Place your thumb on the map at the point where you are standing now.	Yes/No	Yes/No	Yes/No
(c) *Where is your destination?* Select an attack point.	Yes/No	Yes/No	Yes/No
(d) *How will you get there?* Identify a route to your destination, which you can follow confidently and safely. Use handrails, where possible. Thumb your way around the course: place your thumb at your present or last-known position on the map, and read the map in front of your thumb.	Yes/No	Yes/No	Yes/No
(e) *What will you see along the way?* Identify major check-off features.	Yes/No	Yes/No	Yes/No
(f) *What will you see if you go too far?* Identify a catching feature beyond the destination.	Yes/No	Yes/No	Yes/No

2. What am I doing well in this activity (refer to the questions above)?

_____

_____

3. What areas do I need to work on?

_____

_____

4. How can I improve on these areas for the next time I do an orienteering course?

_____

_____

4. Orienteering and my 60 minutes of MVPA per day

Orienteering is a great way to be active. To be healthy, we need to do at least 60 minutes of moderate to vigorous physical activity (MVPA) per day. Orienteering can go a long way towards adding up those minutes in an enjoyable way.

> **Remember**: Physical activity is MVPA when we are breathing heavier than normal, our heart is beating faster than normal, and we find it difficult to hold a normal conversation. Look back to p.36 to see the effects of physical activity on the body as intensity changes.

Task

Page 195 shows a blank orienteering template for you and your partner to design and complete.

- Design a seven-control, line orienteering course.

- Indicate a triangle as your start point and a double circle as your finish point.

- Do the event twice: once at your normal pace, and a second time as fast as you can go!

- Record your heart rate (HR) three times – before the course, at the end of the first course, and at the end of the second course.

  Complete the HR table on p.195. Then answer the questions.

Orienteering and MVPA

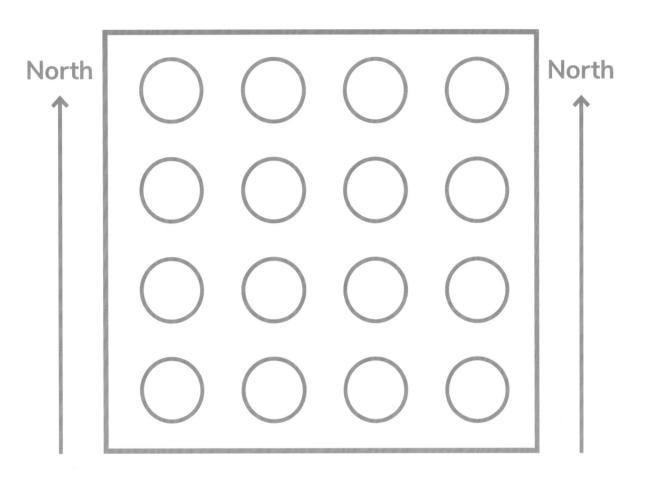

North

North

HR before the course	HR after attempt 1	HR after attempt 2

1. You measured your heart rate three times. Did it go up or down? Explain why you think this happened.

   _____

   _____

2. In your opinion, did you reach MVPA the second time you did the course? How can you tell?

   _____

   _____

3. What happened to the accuracy of your navigation when you tried to do the course really quickly?

   _____

   _____

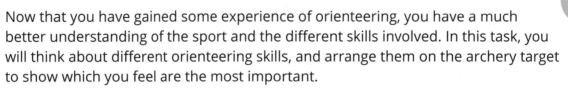

5. Archery target

Now that you have gained some experience of orienteering, you have a much better understanding of the sport and the different skills involved. In this task, you will think about different orienteering skills, and arrange them on the archery target to show which you feel are the most important.

Task

- Read the list of skills (on the right side of the target).
- Draw a line matching each skill to the part of the target where you think it belongs.
- Place the orienteering skill you believe to be the most important in the centre of the target.
- Place the skills you believe to be less important towards the outer edges.

Archery target

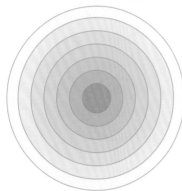

For each skill, draw a line to the area of most importance. (The centre is most important.)

- Map orientation
- Thumbing your map
- Recognising orienteering symbols
- Following a route
- Using handrails
- Have standard procedures for all events
- Obeying the country code

1. Which skill did you place at the centre of the target? Why do you think it is the most important?

  _____

  _____

  _____

  _____

  _____

2. Which skill do you find the most difficult when orienteering? What could you do to get better at it?

  _____

  _____

  _____

  _____

6. Group grading

Problem-solving is a key skill that can be applied across all subject areas in school, and in life in general. It makes sense that the better we are at solving problems, the more likely we are to do well in the things we do! In this task, you will work with a group to identify areas where you can improve your problem-solving skills.

Task

- Complete the team challenge set by your teacher.
- Read the statements in the left-hand column of the table below.
- Tick one of the three categories (Excellent/Good/Needs work).
- Read your answers, and discuss them with your group. Then answer the questions below.

	Excellent	Good	Needs work
I have worked with the group during the activity			
I have shown patience			
I have contributed ideas to improve or change			
I have listened to others			
I have encouraged others			

1. Did your teammates agree with all your answers, and did you agree with their answers? Explain.

    _____

    _____

    _____

2. What have you learned about yourself from doing this task?

    _____

    _____

    _____

3. Describe any areas outside school life that may benefit from the problem-solving skills you used today.

    _____

    _____

    _____

7. Team challenge

Team challenges will help you understand a little bit more about working with others, and how to communicate, cooperate and interact in a team setting. This task helps you to develop problem-solving, reasoning, and social skills. It also tests your ability to discuss, cooperate and work with others who may not always have the same opinion as you!

Task 1

- Take part in the team challenge. (Your teacher will explain how this works.)

- Then work with your group to develop a new team challenge of your own, using whatever equipment is available.

- Before you start your team challenge, answer the questions in the table below.

- When you have designed your team challenge, practise it. When your team is happy with the challenge, present it to the class.

Our team challenge	
Question	**Answer**
What is our challenge?	
What are the different ways that this challenge could be solved?	
What is the best and safest way to solve this challenge? (Note: the whole group has to agree on this point!)	
Who will do what?	

Task 2

1. For each statement below, tick 'Strongly agree', 'Agree', 'Disagree' or 'Strongly disagree'.

Our group	Strongly agree	Agree	Disagree	Strongly disagree
We cooperated well	☐	☐	☐	☐
We communicated well	☐	☐	☐	☐
We listened to each other	☐	☐	☐	☐
We made decisions together	☐	☐	☐	☐
We trusted each other	☐	☐	☐	☐
We thought carefully about safety	☐	☐	☐	☐
We developed a good challenge	☐	☐	☐	☐
We came up with a good solution to the challenge	☐	☐	☐	☐

2. What skills did you call on when designing the team challenge?

_____

_____

3. Was there anything you (personally) found difficult during the task?

_____

_____

_____

4. Did you learn anything new about working with your classmates?

_____

_____

_____

8. How am I doing?

Being active outdoors can really help you to feel well physically, and in other ways too. Complete this questionnaire at the start of the class. Be as honest and as accurate as you can. You will complete this same questionnaire later.

Task

- Look at the scale below. Number 1 represents 'Not true for me'. Number 4 represents 'Really true for me'.

- At the start of class, complete the 'Start of class' column. Then cover your answers.

- Enjoy your physically active class!

- After class, complete the 'After class' column.

- Then look at your answers for both columns. For each column, calculate your total score.

Not true for me   Really true for me

1 ————————— 2 ————————— 3 ————————— 4

	Start of class					After class			
Life is good for me at the moment	1	2	3	4		1	2	3	4
I am fairly treated	1	2	3	4		1	2	3	4
I am quite proud of myself	1	2	3	4		1	2	3	4
I have friends in my class	1	2	3	4		1	2	3	4
I learn from my mistakes	1	2	3	4	**PE class**	1	2	3	4
I have lots of fun	1	2	3	4		1	2	3	4
I am good at learning new things	1	2	3	4		1	2	3	4
I feel safe in my PE class	1	2	3	4		1	2	3	4
My total score:									

1. Compare your score for 'Start of class' with your score for 'After class'. How did you feel after an active PE class? Why was this the case?

_____

_____

2. In your opinion, what is meant by the phrase: 'A healthy mind in a healthy body'?

_____

9. Survival

Wilderness survival may never have crossed your mind before – unless you watch Bear Grylls or Ray Mears on TV! In today's world, basic survival skills probably seem less important, since we all have a wide range of technologies at our fingertips. However, learning survival skills is a fantastic personal challenge. It gives you the chance to connect with nature, become more independent and help others. In this task, you will challenge yourself to 'think outside the box' about everyday items and how they might help you in a disaster scenario.

Task 1: Survival scenario

• Your teacher will divide your class into groups of 4–6.

• Your group will be given a survival scenario and a list of 12 survival tools. You will rank these tools in order of importance, and write down as many uses for the items as you can.

• Your group will collect as many survival tools as you can by playing a game of Rob the Nest. Your group will compete with other groups to collect these tools during Rob the Nest.

• Your teacher will explain the rankings for each tool. You will add up two scores: first for your initial rankings, and second for your collected items.

• Then you will compare the rankings and reflect on the task.

You and your companions have just survived a crash in a small plane. Neither the pilot nor the co-pilot survived the crash. It is mid-January and you are in Northern Canada. The daily temperature is –10°C. The night time temperature is –40°C. There is snow on the ground. The countryside is wooded, with several creeks criss-crossing the area. The nearest town is 30 km away. You are all dressed in city clothes, appropriate for a business meeting.

- Your group of survivors has managed to salvage 12 items, listed in the table on p.203.

- Work as a group to list the 12 items in order of importance for your survival.

- List any practical uses for each item.

- You **must** come to an agreement as a group. When you have ranked your survival tools, write a use for each one.

Task 2: Rob the Nest

- Play Rob the Nest. Your teacher will explain the rules.

- Gather as many survival tools as possible.

- Use the table on p.203 to list and rank all the tools you collected.

Survival tools	Use	Our rank	Actual rank	We collected
A ball of steel wool				
A small axe				
A loaded .45-caliber pistol				
A tin of coconut oil				
Newspapers (one per person)				
Family-size chocolate bars (one per person)				
A cigarette lighter (without fluid)				
An extra shirt and trousers for each survivor				
A piece of heavy-duty canvas (6 m x 6 m)				
A sectional air-map made of plastic				
1 litre of 100-proof whiskey				
A compass				

1 = most important   12 = least important

Comparing rankings

- Compare your rankings with those of the experts (your teacher will provide the experts' rankings).
- Each item is worth points.
- To find your Total Ranking Score, add the points for your top-five ranked items.
- To find your Total Collected Score, add the points for your top-five collected items.
- Answer the questions below.

Total Ranking Score	Total Collected Score

1. Did your group survive, based on ranking the 12 items? Why/why not?

2. Did your group survive, based on items collected? Why/why not?

3. Were there any items your group could not agree on, in terms of ranking? Why?

4. Do you disagree with any of the rankings? Explain.

5. Do you think you have the skills to survive in the wild? Explain.

6. With your partner, discuss your survival strengths and weaknesses.

10. Campcraft

Campcraft is the knowledge and skill required for an outdoor life that lacks modern conveniences. This task gives you the chance to think about getting closer to nature. You will learn about using your own resources and natural resources when camping in the wild.

One of the most important messages for all campers is: **Leave No Trace**. This is an outdoor ethics programme that ensures we preserve the natural environment, minimise damage and maximise safety for everyone. The Leave No Trace programme exists to educate people about humans' recreational impact on nature.

At the heart of the Leave No Trace programme are seven principles for reducing the damage caused by outdoor activities.

1. Plan ahead and prepare.
2. Be considerate of others.
3. Respect farm animals and wildlife.
4. Travel and camp on durable ground.

5. Leave what you find.
6. Dispose of waste properly.
7. Minimise the effects of fire.

Note: Leave No Trace Ireland has a website that can help you to complete the quiz supplied by your teacher.

IRELAND
leave no trace

1. Relay race and quiz. _____

2. Choosing a tent. _____

3. Erecting a tent. _____

4. Choosing a camp location. _____

5. Reflection. _____

Task 1: Relay race and quiz

For this task:

- Your teacher will divide the class into small groups. You will take part in a relay and answer a series of multiple choice questions.

- You will run to your quiz sheet, read the first question carefully, then report back to your group with the question and possible answers.

- When you all agree on an answer, the next person runs back to your quiz sheet to record the answer, and collect the next question.

- Keep going until you have answered all questions.

- Your teacher will check your answers and allow you to make corrections.

- The first group to correctly answer all questions gets to go first in the next activity.

Task 2: Choosing a tent

Once you have answered all your questions correctly, you may choose a tent from the variety supplied. Your group must agree on the tent choice.

1. Which tent did you choose: _____

2. Why did you choose it? (Think about safety, shelter, access, etc.)

   _____
   _____
   _____
   _____
   _____

Task 3: Erecting a tent

Work together to erect the tent.

Task 4: Choosing a camp location

Now that your tent is up, imagine you are going camping. You need to decide where to pitch the tent.

- Work with your group. Look at the map below and choose where you would set up camp.

- Explain your decision in the box below.

- On the map below, mark where you will pitch your tent.

1. Why did your group choose this spot?

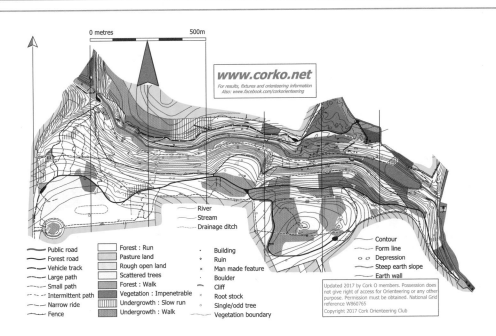

Task 5: Reflection

1. Did you find the quiz easy? Why/why not?

2. Did your group agree quickly on answers and the choice of tent? Why/why not?

3. Did your personal choices in these tasks match the decisions of the group? Why/why not?

End-of-unit assessment 1: Developing team challenges

Throughout this chapter, you have enjoyed various team challenges. In this assessment, you get to create and complete new team challenges for your classmates!

Task 1: Brainstorm the challenges

You and your group will brainstorm four team challenges that you can set up and deliver to the rest of the class. The challenges can be for groups of 4–8 students (your group decides on the number of players). Each challenge must be:

- Enjoyable
- Challenging (hard to figure out)
- Inclusive: everyone in the group can take part
- Easy to explain.

Task 2: Design the challenges

Work with your group to decide on the setup and layout of each challenge. Create a list of specific equipment needed for each event.

	Name of challenge	Equipment	Timing	Safety considerations
Challenge 1				
Challenge 2				
Challenge 3				
Challenge 4				

Task 3: Layout and equipment

Draw diagrams to show how you will lay out the equipment for each challenge, and how you expect each challange to run.

Challenge 1

_____
_____
_____

Challenge 2

_____
_____
_____

Challenge 3

_____
_____
_____

Challenge 4

_____
_____
_____

Task 4: Rate the challenges

Complete each challenge with your group. Use the criteria in the table below to decide which challenge is the best.

Rank the challenges for each of the criteria:

- 1 = Strongly agree
- 2 = Agree
- 3 = Disagree
- 4 = Strongly disagree

	This challenge was enjoyable	This challenge was hard to figure out	This challenge involved everyone	This challenge was easy to explain
Challenge 1				
Challenge 2				
Challenge 3				
Challenge 4				

Task 5

You and your group will lead your whole class in doing one of the challenges – you will be the teachers!

- Every person in your group will be assigned one of these roles:
  - Giving the instructions
  - Ensuring the equipment is okay
  - Monitoring to ensure that nobody is cheating
  - Monitoring to ensure that everyone is safe and is taking part
- Then deliver the challenge to your class.

Task 6

After each group in the class has led a challenge, your class will vote for the best challenge, based on the criteria in Task 4. Remember: you must be able to justify why you have chosen a challenge as the best one!

Challenge group/ name:	This challenge was enjoyable	This challenge was hard to figure out	This challenge involved everyone	This challenge was easy to explain
1				
2				
3				
4				
5				
6				
7				
8				

1. Think about your participation in this assessment. What aspects did you do particularly well?

   _____

   _____

2. Think about your group's participation. What aspects did your group do particularly well?

   _____

   _____

3. What personal skills were useful during the whole task (communicating, listening, etc.)?

   _____

   _____

4. Think about the challenge your group presented. Is there anything you would do to make it better next time?

   _____

   _____

End-of-unit assessment 2: What is orienteering?

In this assessment, you will work in groups of four. Your group will produce a presentation about orienteering, and deliver this presentation to a different group of students! The presentation will be targeted at a group of students who know *nothing* about orienteering.

- You will need to use a video technology as part of this task: part of your presentation needs to show video footage of some orienteering and some reflection.

- Your teacher will give your group an orienteering map and a control card for a course that you will complete.

- Study the map and control card. Note the route you need to take. Then complete the tasks below.

Your presentation criteria

Your group presentation will:

- Use Microsoft PowerPoint (or other software recommended by your teacher)

- Be no more than 5 minutes long

- Combine video footage, pictures and words

- Describe orienteering: explain what it is about, in no more than two sentences!

- Identify five things someone needs to know about orienteering before they take part

- Use video technology to show:

  - What an orienteering map and course looks like

  - How your group went about planning to complete a course

  - What you and your group learned from completing an orienteering course

- Explain why orienteering is a great sport that everyone should try!

- Give all group members an equal opportunity to present

- Be well prepared: clear and easy for the audience to follow

- Catch the interest of the audience

Task 1: Reviewing the course

Consider the orienteering course your teacher has set for your group. Answer the questions below.

1. How many different ways of doing the course can you identify?

   _____

2. Which do you think is the best way of doing it for your group?

   _____

   _____

   _____

Task 2: Recording your presentation

When you are ready, video record your group before you do the course:
- Show the map and course to the camera.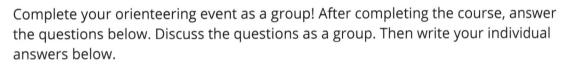

- Explain how your group will complete the course.

- This clip will be no more than 30 seconds, and you will include it in your final presentation.

Complete your orienteering event as a group! After completing the course, answer the questions below. Discuss the questions as a group. Then write your individual answers below.

1. Were you happy with how the course went for you? Why?

   _____

   _____

2. Did you work well with each other as a team?

   _____

   _____

3. What could you do differently to improve your performance on an orienteering course in future?

   _____

   _____

   _____

When you are ready, video record your group after you have done the course:
- 'Debrief' on how the orienteering course went for you.

- Explain how you would improve, if you were to do this assessment again.

- This clip will be no more than 30 seconds, and you will include it in your final presentation.

Task 3: Editing your presentation

Put together your presentation. Refer to the presentation criteria on p.212 and use the video clips you recorded.

* Decide who will deliver which part of the presentation. It can help if you think of your presentation in four different parts: each person gets one part to present, and everyone has an equal amount of time to talk.

* When you present, you want it to run smoothly. Each presenter takes over from the previous presenter without stopping the presentation for too long.

* Use the box below to plan the order of your presentation.

Presentation order	Who will present this part? What will they cover?
Part 1	
Part 2	
Part 3	
Part 4	

Task 4: Reflecting

Give your presentation to the class group that your teacher has selected.
Then answer the questions below.

1. What were you happiest about in your orienteering presentation experience?

2. What did you learn from this experience?

3. Give one piece of advice to a new group doing this assessment.

4. How could you use your learning from this experience in a new or similar experience?

Strand review
In this chapter, you learned about:

- Orienteering strategies and map-reading skills ☐
- Completing line orienteering events safely and confidently ☐
- Being technically competent, for your level of experience and potential ☐
- The amount of physical activity that is necessary for a full and healthy life that includes the outdoors ☐
- Contributing to team challenges using your skills for feedback, cooperation and problem-solving ☐

- Reflecting and evaluating on your personal contribution and your team's effectiveness in completing an adventure experience ☐
- Self-assessing an adventure experience to improve your attitude towards further involvement ☐
- Using a full value contract (FVC) to identify your responsibilities for personal and social behaviour in adventure activity settings ☐

Look back over the activities you completed. Tick the skills you used.

Managing Myself		Staying Well		Managing Information and Thinking		Being Numerate	
I know myself better	☐	I am healthy and active	☐	I gathered and analysed information	☐	I estimated, predicted and calculated	☐
I made decisions	☐	I am social	☐	I thought creatively	☐	I was interested in problem-solving	☐
I set goals	☐	I am safe	☐	I thought about what I learned	☐		
I achieved goals	☐	I feel confident	☐				
I thought about what I learned		I feel positive about what I learned	☐	I used digital technology to access, manage and share information	☐		
I used technology to learn	☐						

Being Creative		Working with Others		Communicating		Being Literate	
I thought about things from a different point of view	☐	I developed relationships	☐	I listened to my classmates	☐	I understood some new words	☐
I put ideas into action	☐	I dealt with conflict	☐	I expressed myself	☐	I wrote for different reasons	☐
I learned in a creative way	☐	I cooperated	☐	I performed/ presented	☐	I expressed my ideas clearly	☐
I was creative with digital technology	☐	I respected difference	☐	I had a discussion/ debate	☐	I developed my spoken language	☐
		I learned with others	☐	I used digital technology to communicate	☐	I read and wrote in different ways	☐
		I worked with others using digital technology	☐				

Discuss two skills (above) that you intend to focus on more in the future.

_____

_____

_____

_____

Dance

Chapter 07

Introduction

Dance is very much part of a broad and balanced PE programme. Dance has the potential to improve your movement, and how often you move. You will be creating, performing and appreciating dance throughout this chapter. This will help to improve your ability to express yourself and to communicate with others in your class.

There are many styles of dance, including ballet, tap, jazz, folk, contemporary, ballroom and hip hop. Participating in dance, and achieving a high level of skill in any or all of the different areas of dance, will improve your performance in other sporting areas. This is because the basic skills and qualities are easily transferrable to other sporting and recreational activities.

Common terms

Aesthetic	Concerned with beauty or the appreciation of beauty
Actions	Activities that require you to cooperate and problem-solve with others to achieve a common goal
Space	The direction taken within a dance (e.g. floor patterns and levels)
Dynamics	How you change the movement within a dance (e.g. flow, speed and power)
Relationships	With whom and what: the order of phrases within a dance, and the formations with a partner or group of dancers
Choreography	To plan and arrange the movements, steps and patterns of dancers
Beat	The steady, repeating pulse in music

Assessment tools

1. Introduction to dance

Task 1

In this task, you will learn how your class can develop new body movements and vocabulary to help you express your ideas in dance.

1. With a partner, think of one move to suit each element in the table below.

2. Perform the move, describe it and tick the box when you have completed it.

3. Then choose five elements, overall, from the box. Choreograph a short partner-dance that uses these five elements.

Actions (What)	Describe	Tick
Travel (e.g. turn or jump): think of travelling in gymnastics)		
Repetition		
Aesthetic: looks pleasing to the eye		
Space (Where)		
Change the direction of travel		
Follow a floor pattern		
Change the level		
Dynamics (How)		
Change the speed (e.g. faster to slower)		
Change the power (e.g. forceful to gentle)		
Relationships (With whom/what)		
Unison (together at the same time)		
Canon (one after the other: coming in at regular or irregular intervals)		
Meeting and parting		
Mirroring (reverse image)		

Task 2

At the beginning of your dance classes, your teacher may use a variety of introductory activities to warm up the body and to get you thinking and talking about dance with your classmates and teacher. You will see how your dance classes can improve your understanding of your own body.

Your teacher will choose an introductory activity for the class. Follow the instructions below to complete the activity. Focus on the changes that happen to your body as you move.

1. When your teacher asks you, measure your heart rate, measure your breathing rate, and note your rate of perceived exertion. It is interesting to see how these change, based on how hard or how easy the activity was.

Note: If you need help with this, see p.36 for effects of physical activity on the body as intensity changes.

2. Record your results in the table below.

Introductory activity	Heart rate (HR) (beats per minute)	Breathing rate (BR) (breaths per minute)	Rate of perceived exertion (RPE)
Before dance activity			
After dance activity			

Reflection

1. Describe what happened to your HR, BR, and RPE rates as the introductory activity progressed.

_____

_____

_____

2. Why did this happen? Explain.

_____

_____

_____

3. Can you think of any other common dances that might be good as a warm-up activity?

_____

_____

_____

2. Beats and count

Music can be broken into two-part rhythms and three-part rhythms. For example, we can count sets of 4 and sets of 8 (two-part rhythms) in most pop music. We can count sets of 3 and sets of 6 (three-part rhythms) in waltzes.

Try counting two-part rhythms in a pop song you know: can you count sets of 8 regular beats? Counting the beats in music helps you to recognise and dance to the rhythm of the song.

Task 1

The Macarena was made for counting beats!

1. First, dance along to the song for about a minute, using the Macarena movements to help you recognise the beat. You will notice that you perform and repeat 16 movements throughout the song. The movements make up two sets of 8 beats.

2. Listen again, without dancing. Try to identify the 8 beats without moving.

3. Count out the 8 beats as you hear them.

4. Click your fingers or clap your hands along with the beat.

5. Now see if you can get your toes tapping along to the beat.

You can put this into practice with other songs. Choose another song and see if you can find the 8-beat count. Can you do the Macarena dance to the beat of the new song?

Task 2

Work in groups of four. Make up a short, simple dance with different movements that could help you to find the beat in other songs.

1. Your teacher will choose a song for the class.

2. Use your movements to dance along to the beat of the music. Repeat your 8-count dance throughout the song.

3. How many other songs can you dance to using your 8-count repetition?

4. In your group of four, try doing your dance in canon:
    - One person starts the dance
    - After 8 beats, the second person joins in
    - After another 8 beats, the third person joins in
    - 8 counts later, all of you will be dancing.

5. Describe your eight movements:

    (a) _____

    (b) _____

    (c) _____

    (d) _____

    (e) _____

    (f) _____

    (g) _____

    (h) _____

6. List five songs you found that you could dance to, in time with the beat.

    _____

    _____

    _____

Reflection

1. In the table below, circle the answer that applies to you.

I found this task	Easy	OK	Difficult
I can recognise the beat in music	Always	Sometimes	Never
I can dance to the beat in music	Always	Sometimes	Never

2. List some tips for helping you to find the beat of a piece of music.

    _____

    _____

3. Styles of dance 1

Task 1

Unscramble and match these anagrams of popular styles of dance.

Anagrams		Answers
Phi pho		Ballet
Carpentry moo		Ballroom
Lab let		Swing
Wings		Hip hop
Kolf		Tap
All broom		Folk
Pat		Contemporary

Task 2

Search online for the video 'Evolution of Dance'.

1. How many of the styles of dance you can identify?

2. The dance is 6 minutes long. Your teacher will divide your class into six groups. Each group will take one minute of the dance and create a choreography for it. Adjust the dance to suit your group's ability. Perform the dance, group by group.

3. This dance is over ten years old and there are many styles missing from this performance.
   - Work with your group to brainstorm some of the missing styles.

   - Choreograph a short dance that you could add to the original, which will include two of the missing styles. Your added dance will last a maximum of 45 seconds.

   Note any missing styles here.

   _____

   _____

   _____

   _____

4. Work with your partner to list any other styles of dance you can think of.
   - **Think:** Make your own list first.

   - **Pair:** Discuss your ideas with your partner.

   - **Share:** Work with your partner to share your ideas with the class.

Dance Styles

4. Styles of dance 2

Task 1

Look back to Task 2 on p.223. Choose any style of dance, and plan a warm-up for this style.

1. Your dance warm-up should start as low-intensity and work to high-intensity.

2. Your warm-up should incorporate movements from the style of dance you have selected.

3. Your warm-up should be no more than 3 minutes long.

4. In the box below, write notes and draw diagrams to explain your dance warm-up.

5. Record your HR before and after your warm-up.

> **Note:** If you need help with this, see p.49 for planning a warm-up or cool-down.

My dance warm-up

Reflection

1. Write five things you know about warming up.

_____

_____

_____

_____

_____

Identify your style: _____

Note your HR before your warm-up: _____

Note your HR after your warm-up: _____

2. Do you think your warm-up worked well? Why/why not?

_____

_____

_____

_____

3. Could you use this warm-up for other activities? How?

_____

_____

_____

_____

5. Choreography

If you are new to dance, it can be difficult to remember all the information you need to know when planning, creating and performing your own dance. The fish bone graphic (below) is a useful tool. Fill it out as you progress through Chapter 7. It will show you, at a glance, all the components of dance. This will be a useful memory aid.

Task 1

Write each word from the blue box under the correct heading in the fish bone.

- Travel
- Turning
- Stillness
- Gesture
- Body shape
- Ballroom
- Modern (hip hop)
- Elevation
- Mirroring

- Level
- Face a different way
- Speed (slow/quick)
- Power (forceful/gentle)
- Sharper/softer
- Flow (bound/free)
- Meeting and parting
- Unison
- Canon

- Formations
- Size of a movement
- Folk
- Direction
- Creative
- Ballet
- Impulsive/sustained

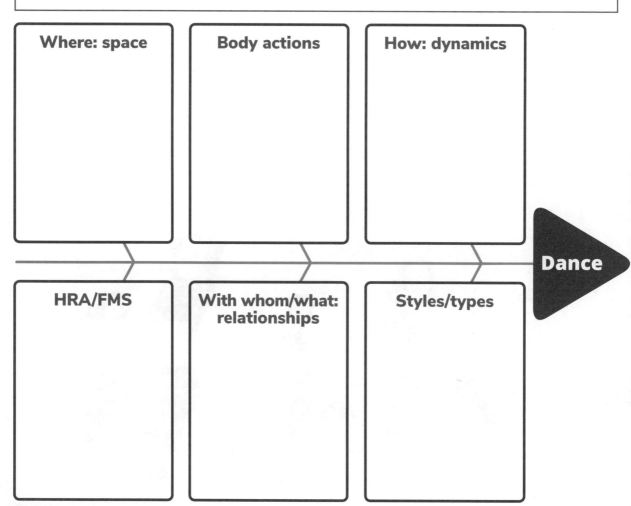

Task 2

Use the ideas from your fish bone to design and choreograph a short partner-dance that showcases the skills you have learned so far. The subheadings in the blue bubble will help you.

1. Make sure your dance has a theme.

2. Perform your dance for a pair of classmates. Use their feedback to improve your dance.

3. Team up with a different pair of classmates. Teach each other your dances.

4. Now combine both dances to form one longer dance. Adjust the dance, as appropriate, to suit one theme.

5. Briefly describe your finished, four-person dance in the space below. Use bullet points, keywords or sketches.

6. Video analysis

Building on your dance from assessment tool 5

You may have a picture in your head of what you look like when you are performing an activity or dance ... but is this what you actually look like? In this assessment, you will learn to use digital technology to video yourself and your group. You can watch the video to see how well you are doing and to improve your performance.

Task

1. Ask a classmate to record you and your group performing your dance (from Task 2 on p.227).

2. Keep the performance short: maximum 2 minutes. (Nobody wants to watch long videos of an assessment tool over and over!)

Reflection

1. Reflect on your performance in the table below. You can use some or all of the criteria.

Actions (What)	Present	Absent
Uses repetition of the same body parts		
Changes the body part used to make the action		
Adds a travel, turn, jump, balance, stillness or gesture		

Space (Where)	Present	Absent
Changes the direction of travel		
Follows a floor pattern		
Changes the level		

Dynamics (How)	Present	Absent
Changes the flow (bound/free)		
Changes the speed (faster/slower)		
Changes the power (forceful/gentle)		

Relationships (With whom/what)	Present	Absent
Unison (together at the same time)		
Canon (one after the other: coming in at regular or irregular intervals)		
Meeting and parting		
Mirroring (reverse image)		

2. What is the use of recording your performances? Complete the table below.

Positives of using technology in dance	Challenges of using technology in dance
•	•
•	•
•	•

3. In what other ways could you use digital technology in PE?

_____

_____

_____

_____

7. Formations and dance map

Most dances are designed to be aesthetically pleasing. Dancers use a variety of formations, as well as themes, actions, levels and directions. All these elements contribute to the aesthetics.

CIRCLE

SQUARE

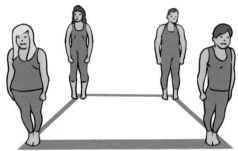

TRIANGLE

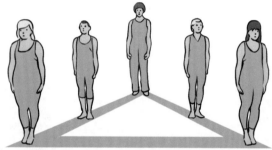

LINES

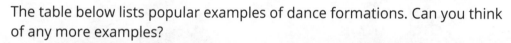

Task 1

The table below lists popular examples of dance formations. Can you think of any more examples?

Formation	Example	Your example
Circle	Ring-a-Ring o' Roses	
Square	American square dance	
Triangle	Beyoncé: 'Single Ladies'	
Line	Macarena	

Task 2

Work in groups of four to create a dance. Include at least one of the formations from the table on p.230. When you create your dance, include different body actions and explore the space around you. This assessment will help you to see the floor patterns, formations and body actions you use in your own dance routine.

Instructions

1. In the box below, create a line drawing of the pathways you travelled in your dance. Also write the movements you used during your dance.

2. Your line drawing will be unique to your dance.

3. You can draw/write from memory after performing. Alternatively, ask a classmate to record you, and then draw/write as you watch the footage.

4. Below is a sample dance map which will help you to visualise your completed dance map.

Start   Run   Skip   Skip   Slide sideways   Spin   End with jump and land   Tall shape

Reflection

1. Think about mapping your movements in other activities. How might it help you to improve?

_____

_____

_____

8. Dancing for my health!

Being active in dance will make you sweat and will get you moving at a moderate to vigorous physical activity (MVPA) intensity. This will add to your 60 minutes of physical activity a day. In this assessment, you will learn how to use a dice and some basic actions to create a dance routine that will get your heart pumping!

Task

1. Work in groups to create a dance routine. Roll a dice to decide on the actions you will use. You will roll the dice a total of six times to figure out what to do and in what order. For example:
    *   If you roll a 1, your group must perform a spin.
    *   If you roll a 2, your group must perform a jump, and so on.

2. Use the graphic below to record the six actions you will include in your group dance.

Actions

1. Spin
2. Jump
3. Turn
4. Roll
5. Balance
6. Gesture (an isolated movement)

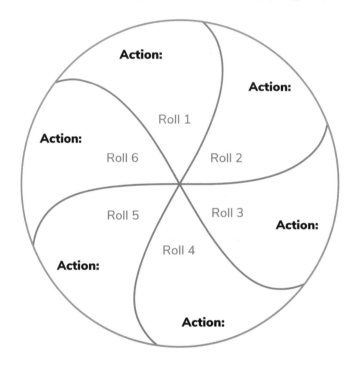

3. Start at a light intensity. Gradually increase the intensity to become more difficult. Your dance lasts 2 minutes in total.

4. When you have completed your dance routine, note your rate of perceived exertion in the table on p.233.

Note: If you need help with this, see p.36 for effects of physical activity on the body as intensity changes.

Intensity zone	Rating	Description	Rate of perceived exertion (RPE) for my dance routine
Sedentary		**Doing nothing** I am sitting down and watching TV.	
Light		**Really easy** I could do this in my sleep.	
		Easy I'm comfortable: I could do this pace all day.	
		Not so easy This is still easy-ish, but I am starting to feel a bit warmer and I'm breathing a little harder.	
Moderate		**Getting hard** I'm starting to sweat a little and breathe a little faster, but I can still talk comfortably.	
		Pretty hard I'm sweating more now and breathing faster, but can still talk.	
		Hard I'm getting a bit breathless now and I'm sweating. It's not easy to have a conversation.	
Vigorous		**Really hard** I'm even more out of breath. It's very hard to talk. Really sweating now.	
		Really really hard I'm almost out of breath, the most I could give now is a one-word answer.	
		On the verge I'm completely out of breath. I can't talk.	
		Unsustainable! I have collapsed!	

Reflection

1. What type of movements got your heart pumping the most?

_____

2. How would you make your dance routine even more intense for your heart and lungs? What kind of movements could you add?

_____

_____

9. Dance and FMS

Dance is a wonderful way to teach movements and words to people of all abilities. Think of some favourite songs from childhood, e.g. 'The Birdie Song' or 'The Hokey Pokey'.

Now it's your turn to think of a dance to help others to learn.

Task

For this task, you will look back to Chapter 1. You will design a dance based on the theme of FMS. Your goal is to select and incorporate five FMS into a dance that could be taught to primary school pupils to increase their FMS in a new, fun way.

Choose a formation from Assessment 7 (p.230) and base your dance around it. Keep your dance short and simple – and use as much repetition as you can.

Instructions

1. Briefly outline your dance in the table below.

Dance name	
Song	
Five FMS	1. 2. 3. 4. 5.

2. When all groups have designed their dances, perform them for the class. Take a vote in your class to decide the favourite dance. This group will teach the whole class how to do the dance. Reflect on your experience below.

Reflection

It is important to be able to work with others, and to be able to reflect on this. It will help your group to plan, create and perform better dances. After a group performance, this reflection exercise will support you in assessing how well you worked with your group.

1. Read the statements in the table on p.235. You will see that many of the statements are similar.

2. Think about how you worked with your group. Circle the statements that best apply to you. Circle **one** statement per row.

3. Compare your answers to the answers of other students in your group.

I worked with the group all the time	I worked with the group some of the time	I rarely worked with the group	I created conflict in the group
I was patient with everyone in the group	I showed impatience once	I showed impatience on more than one occasion	I was consistently impatient
I contributed ideas	I contributed some ideas	I contributed few ideas	I did not contribute any ideas
I listened to everyone in the group	I listened most times	I listened sometimes	I never listened
I was encouraging to everyone in the group	I encouraged most of the time	I encouraged sometimes	I never encouraged

4. (a) Do you think children would enjoy learning your dance? Why?

_____

(b) How would your dance help their skill development?

_____

(c) In your opinion, why do children like learning through dance?

_____

5. (a) Outline any comparisons between your answers and the answers of other people in your group.

_____

_____

(b) How could you improve the way you work with others in the future?

_____

_____

_____

_____

_____

_____

_____

_____

10. Lucky dip

In this assessment, you will put into practice everything you have learned so far.

Task

1. Each person in your class takes five blank pieces of paper and writes:
   - One theme
   - One shape
   - One style
   - One relationship (e.g. unison or canon)
   - One formation.

2. Your teacher will place the pieces of paper into hats: one for themes, one for shapes, etc.

3. Work in groups of five (or smaller). Each group will choose one piece of paper from each hat.

4. When your group has chosen its five pieces of paper, you will use these pointers to choreograph a short dance that showcases these five elements.

5. Your group has just 5 minutes to create the dance!

6. Before the dances are performed, work with your class to create a suitable evaluation. You will choose what criteria to look for and how to grade the dance. Look back through this chapter to help you decide on the criteria.

7. Write the evaluation criteria in the box below.

8. Then watch and evaluate each group's dance.

Reflection

1. Describe your dance.

Song	
Theme	
Shape	
Style	
Relationship	
Formation	

2. This task was done in a very limited time. How did your group feel about working to a deadline?

_____

_____

3. What was your favourite part of this task? Why?

_____

_____

4. Was there anything you did not enjoy about this task? Why?

_____

_____

End-of-unit assessment 1: Appreciating dance

Your teacher will divide your class into groups of 4–6 for this assessment.

In **Task 1**, you will create and perform a group dance. This dance will include at least:

- Five body actions
- Three different levels
- A variation in the dynamics (faster/slower)
- Two different formations.

You will record your dance so that you can evaluate it.

In **Task 2**, you will evaluate your performance.

In **Task 3**, you will identify any improvements that can be made to your performance. You will write a record of the improvements, refine your dance in the next lesson and make another video recording.

In **Task 4**, you will submit a video to your teacher that evaluates your dance. In your video, you will explain your evaluation of your performance.

In **Task 5**, you will write a brief reflection of your experience. You will outline how you felt about creating a dance, working in a group, what you found difficult or challenging, and what you would do differently next time.

Task 1: Description of my dance

Describe how your dance will look. Use sentences and bullet points, or draw sketches.

Element	Description
Body actions	
Levels	
Dynamics	
Formations	

Task 2: Evaluation of my dance

	Excellent	Good	Needs work
I willingly supported others in the group	☐	☐	☐
I contributed to the dance	☐	☐	☐
I could explain the dance	☐	☐	☐
I performed the dance sequence with ease	☐	☐	☐

Task 3: Improvements made to my dance

Describe how your performance went and how you could improve it.

1. Were you happy with your performance?

   _____

2. How could you improve it?

   _____

   _____

   _____

3. Were there any aspects of this task you found difficult?

   _____

   _____

Task 4: Notes for my evaluation video

Answer the questions below to describe your dance and how you felt it went.

1. Did you include all the elements from Task 1?

   _____

2. Did you use a wide range of body movements?

   _____

3. Did you use all the space available to you? Think of your dance map from p.231.

   _____

4. Were your movements in time with the beat of the music?

   _____

Task 5: Reflection

1. How did you feel about creating a dance?

   _____

   _____

2. How did you feel about working in a group?

   _____

   _____

3. What did you find difficult or challenging?

   _____

   _____

4. What would you do differently next time?

   _____

   _____

End-of-unit assessment 2: So you think you can dance?

This is a group task that will take place at the end of your dance module. Your teacher will assign you to groups.

For this assessment, each week all groups in your class choreograph a dance based on different themes:

- Dance 1: Superheroes

- Dance 2: International

- Dance 3: Choice. *After Dance 2, your class will work together to decide the theme for Dance 3.*

Weekly criteria

Each dance will meet the following criteria:
- It will be approximately 1–3 minutes long.
- It will include formations (see p.230).
- It will involve movements made in time with the beat of the music.
- It will suit all abilities within the group.

- At the end of each week, the whole class will evaluate the groups on their dance, using the table on p.242.

- The class will vote and decide on the score for each element of the dance, giving each group a score out of 25 every week.
  Green light = 5 points, Amber light = 3 points, Red light = 1 point.

- Your teacher will note the scoring table and the scores on the board each week.

- After your dance, you will reflect on your individual performance and your group performance. This is really important because it gives you the chance to improve on your weaknesses and maximise your strengths for the next dance.

- Your teacher will keep track of the scores and, by the end of the final week, an overall winning group will be decided.

Task 1: Description of my dance

Plan, choreograph and practise your dance, using the weekly criteria (above). Briefly describe your dance. Include the formations that will be used.

Dance 1	Dance 2	Dance 3

Task 2: Whole-class evaluation of my dance

Each group will use the table below to evaluate each dance – one table per group.
If there are five groups in your class, Group 1 will be evaluated by Groups 2–5.

Element		5 pts	3 pts	1 pts
Theme	Easy to identify	○	○	○
Duration	1–3 mins long	○	○	○
Formations	Many interesting and neat formations	○	○	○
Coordination	Coordinated movements in sync with the beat	○	○	○
Participation	All members of the group performed each element of the dance well	○	○	○
Total score		/25		

Task 3: Reflecting on the performance

Reflect on your performance each week. You won't see yourself performing, so you
will need to reflect on how you felt and how you thought the performance went. Take
on board any feedback from the group as a whole.

Reflection: Dance 1		
Group name:	Song choice:	Theme:
Our score: /25		
Successes		Challenges
What went well for me		What went well for our group
What I could improve on		What we can improve on
Top three tips for our next performance:		

Reflection: Dance 2

Group name:	Song choice:	Theme:

Our score: /25

Successes	Challenges
What went well for me	What went well for our group
What I could improve on	What we can improve on

Top three tips for our next performance:

Reflection: Dance 3

Group name:	Song choice:	Theme:

Our score: /25

Successes	Challenges
What went well for me	What went well for our group
What I could improve on	What we can improve on

Top three tips for our next performance:

Overall reflection

At the end of the assessment, reflect on the whole process.

Group name:

Do you think you improved each week? Why/why not?

What was the most difficult part of this task? Why?

What did you enjoy most about it? Why?

Do you think 'competing' against other groups each week was helpful to your own learning and performance? Why/why not?

Strand review

In this chapter, you learned about:

- Enriching personal and social development while interacting with others through dance ☐
- The importance of beats and count in dance ☐
- A range of elements and styles in creating dances ☐
- Appreciating your own performance, based on critique of a recording and feedback from others ☐
- Appreciating your group's talents and strengths through awards, and recognising difference ☐
- Reflecting on your experience of creating and participating in a performance. ☐

Look back over the activities you completed. Tick the skills you used.

Managing Myself	Staying Well	Managing Information and Thinking	Being Numerate
I know myself better ☐	I am healthy and active ☐	I gathered and analysed information ☐	I estimated, predicted and calculated ☐
I made decisions ☐	I am social ☐	I thought creatively ☐	I was interested in problem-solving ☐
I set goals ☐	I am safe ☐	I thought about what I learned ☐	
I achieved goals ☐	I feel confident ☐	I used digital technology to access, manage and share information ☐	
I thought about what I learned ☐	I feel positive about what I learned ☐		
I used technology to learn ☐			

Being Creative	Working with Others	Communicating	Being Literate
I thought about things from a different point of view ☐	I developed relationships ☐	I listened to my classmates ☐	I understood some new words ☐
I put ideas into action ☐	I dealt with conflict ☐	I expressed myself ☐	I wrote for different reasons ☐
I learned in a creative way ☐	I cooperated ☐	I performed/ presented ☐	I expressed my ideas clearly ☐
I was creative with digital technology ☐	I respected difference ☐	I had a discussion/ debate ☐	I developed my spoken language ☐
	I learned with others ☐	I used digital technology to communicate ☐	I read and wrote in different ways ☐
	I worked with others using digital technology ☐		

Discuss two skills (above) that you intend to focus on more in the future.

_____

_____

_____

_____

Gymnastics
Chapter 08

Introduction

Gymnastics teaches us about athleticism and focus. It is a sport of dedication that improves strength, flexibility, balance, coordination and cooperation. It provides the chance to be creative and competitive. It teaches us the importance and usefulness of body control. It teaches us mental concentration and gives us the opportunity to work independently, as well as with others.

Gymnasts compete in a variety of events on different apparatus or equipment, including vault, bars, rings and beam, as well as floor-based routines. Gymnastics will help you to develop your strength, speed, coordination, power, flexibility and mental toughness. Improving any of these areas will allow you to perform at a higher level in other sports too.

Common terms

Theme	The main subject or idea of a piece of work
Aesthetic	The beauty of something
Sequence	A set of related movements that follow each other in a specific order
Fluency	Being able to move smoothly
Symmetry	A shape that is the same on both sides when spilt down the middle
Asymmetry	A shape that is different on each side when split down the middle
Poise	Controlled, graceful, elegant and balanced movements
Perform	To present a sequence to an audience

1. Basics of gymnastics

In this chapter, you will learn new terms, movements and skills that will help you to design, perform and evaluate gymnastic sequences. Let's start with some of the words we will use in gymnastics.

Task

1. Match each term to its meaning. Your teacher will help you with this.

Term	Meaning
Aesthetic	Someone who helps another to achieve a movement
Balance	The beauty of something; pleasing to the eye
Cooperation	Moving through the air
Flexibility	Moving from body part to another
Flight	Moving smoothly and with control
Fluency	Ability to move joints through a wide range of motion
Sequence	Weight is distributed equally
Supporter	A shape (e.g. of the body) that is different on each side
Transfer of weight	A shape (e.g. of the body) that is the same on both sides
Symmetry	Working together
Asymmetry	Movements or actions that follow, one after the other
Travel/locomotion	Continuous movement
Inversion	An idea that runs through a piece of work
Theme	Grace, balance and control in movements
Poise	Being upside down
Muscular tension	One side is the same as the other
Matching	Showing a reflection of something
Mirroring	Muscles stretched tight and held firm
Apparatus	Equipment

2. List at least five forms of travel in gymnastics.

_____

_____

3. Design and perform a short sequence of movement: on your own, with a partner, or in a group.

   Your sequence will contain:
   - Variety: fast and slow movements
   - Use of space: cover as much of the floor as possible
   - Different levels: high and low movements
   - Stillness: freeze in position at some points during your sequence.

   Record your sequence and complete the following table. Tick the boxes to show which elements you included in your sequence. For each type of movement, give one example and a brief description.

Element	✔	Description
Fast movements		
Slow movements		
High-level movements		
Low-level movements		
Stillness		

4. Look at the basic shapes in the images below. How many of these shapes did you make in your sequence? Circle all that apply.

5. Unscramble and match these anagrams of common gymnastics terms.

Anagram	Answer
Quasar beer	Technique
Thiglf	Inversion
Veells	Arabesque
Cab lean	Continuity
Rant rep	Locomotion
Itch queen	Levels
Nine visor	Flight
Airy vet	Balance
Icon nutty	Partner
Coil to moon	Variety

2. Flight

Flight is travelling through the air or jumping. In gymnastics, jumps are used as a form of locomotion, to demonstrate body control and to express different shapes. Jumps can also be useful when linking one movement to another, to maintain fluency within a sequence.

There are three phases in each jump:

- **Take-off:** Controlled and steady – bend the knees and use the arms to gain momentum

- **Flight:** Think about the aesthetics (how the jump looks) while in the air

- **Landing:** Controlled with bent knees to absorb shock and minimise noise

Task

1. Match each term to its meaning. Your teacher will help you with this.

Flight	Get onto a piece of apparatus
Stick	Move through the air
Split	Get off a piece of apparatus
Tuck	Legs spread far apart
Star	Bend at the waist with both legs straight
Layout	Land on two feet after flip or cartwheel
Mount	Controlled landing on two feet
Dismount	Turn the whole body on vertical axis
Pike	Control of body position
Posture	Arms and legs spread wide
Twist	Bend the knees and pull them in to the chest

 FMS The FMS of landing is essential for safety and preventing injury. It is important to master it before working on jumping technique. Go to pp.12–13 and work with a partner to assess your ability to land safely.

2. Now that you have matched each term to its meaning, look at the flight pictures below. How many of these can you perform? Practise with your partner. Tick the ones you can do.

Flight ☐   Stick ☐   Split ☐   Mount ☐

Tuck ☐   Pike ☐   Star ☐

Dismount ☐   Twist ☐

Posture ☐   Layout ☐

3. Name and draw three jumps.

4. (i) Choose one jump and describe how the body looks when performing it. What shapes are made?

_____

_____

(ii) Now try to use your chosen jump to link two movements in a short sequence. Record your short sequence.

(iii) Circle all the elements you spotted in your sequence.

Run-up   Half-pike

              Pencil

One-foot take-off   Other shape   Hard landing

              Tuck

                                Twist (how   Fluid (no break

Two-foot take-off   Pike   many degrees?)   in movement within the

              Straddle   Soft landing   sequence)

Star

5. What else did you notice about your jump? For example: Did you use your arms for momentum? Did you land softly? Was it a one-foot or two-foot landing?

_____

6. How could you improve the jump? Think about how it felt, looked, sounded, linked the movements, etc.

_____

7. Did your jump work as a good link between your movements? Why?

_____

3. Balance 1

In gymnastics, balance is when the body is held steady in a specific position. Balancing requires strength and precision. And when you work with a partner, balance also involves cooperation and trust. Gymnastics is all about controlled body movements. Balance brings beautiful moments of stillness to sequences.

Task

1. Practise and perform the arabesque/airplane balance. Ask your partner to fill in the table below to assess your technique.

Correct technique	●	○	●
Start position			
Is the gymnast standing upright, feet together, arms by side?	○	○	○
Is the head looking forward? Is the spine stretched?	○	○	○
Balance			
Is the weight slowly placed on the foot, which is not lifted?	○	○	○
Is the other leg raised until straight out behind the body, parallel to ground?	○	○	○
Are the toes pointed?	○	○	○
Is the back knee locked straight?	○	○	○
Are the arms spread away from the body, making a T-shape?	○	○	○
Is the chest up, head looking forward?	○	○	○
Is there a 90-degree angle between front and back leg?	○	○	○
Is the balance held without moving for 3 seconds?	○	○	○

> **Note:** Balances can be performed on many **points of contact**. 'Points of contact' means how many body parts are touching the ground/mat. An arabesque involves one point of contact, since only your foot touches the mat.

2. Draw an appropriate balance in each of the spaces below. Practise these balances and tick all the ones you can perform.

Balance with **four** points of contact ☐

Balance with **three** points of contact ☐

Balance with **two** points of contact ☐

Balance with **one** point of contact ☐

3. Unscramble these anagrams of common gymnastics terms.

Anagram		Answer
Able can		routine
Real pall		stretched
Our nite		contact
In top		balance
Tech drest		qualities
Cant cot		perform
I squat lie		point
Mr Re Fop		parallel

4. Rotation

Rotation refers to a wide variety of movement patterns that require the body to turn in a circle around a fixed point. This includes twisting, rolling, turning and spinning. Rolls, cartwheels and handsprings are all examples of rotation in gymnastics.

Task 1

1. Research the following rolls online. Circle each roll that you can complete.

Log/pencil roll

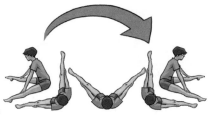

Teddy bear roll

Side roll

Forward roll   Straddle roll   Forward roll to standing

Backward roll

Backward roll to standing

2. Practise and perform a forward roll to standing. Use the technique checklist below to assess your technique or your partner's technique.

Correct technique			
Start position			
Is the gymnast standing at the end of the mat, along the narrow side?	○	○	○
Does the gymnast squat down and place palms on the edge of the mat, with fingers facing away?	○	○	○
Are the elbows bent forward? Is the weight put on the hands?	○	○	○
Roll			
Is the chin tucked in to the chest?	○	○	○
Are the legs extended? Are the hips above shoulder level?	○	○	○
Does the gymnast push off the ground, with feet and head tucked between arms?	○	○	○
Does the gymnast place the weight on the back of the shoulders – not the head or the neck? (The head should not touch the mat.)	○	○	○
Does the gymnast keep the roll going, so the hips pass over the head and the roll goes along the spine?	○	○	○
Does the gymnast keep the body in a tucked position (does not straighten out)?	○	○	○
Finish			
Are the feet placed flat on the floor, tucked in as close as possible to the body?	○	○	○
Are the arms stretched upwards and forwards to achieve a standing position, without using the hands?	○	○	○

3. (i) Why do you tuck the head under when performing a forward roll?

_____

(ii) Try a log roll with a tight body and then a loose body. Which is better? Why?

_____

(iii) Add a jump before or after your roll. Land with feet together and then land with feet apart. Which is better? Why?

_____

(iv) Being able to control your body is vital in gymnastics and in other sports too. Name some other sports where it is useful to be able to roll.

_____

4. Your teacher will set a rolling-sequence task for you. Listen to your teacher outline the elements you will include in your sequence. Design and practise the sequence. Fill in the table below to describe your sequence.

My sequence	
Element	**Description**
One-roll example	Teddy bear roll

Task 2

Ask your partner to watch your sequence and to fill in the table below to award gold, silver or bronze for each element. In the justification column, your partner will briefly outline why you won gold, silver or bronze.

Criteria	Gold	Silver	Bronze	Justification
All elements were included				
There was control				
There was different use of levels				
The sequence flowed				
There were moments of stillness				

5. Inversion

Inversion is any skill where you are upside down. Usually, this means performing balances such as handstands and headstands. It also includes movements such as cartwheels, tumbles and flips.

Task

1. Perform an inversion.
   - Ask your partner to record you and to use the table below to assess your technique.
   - You can modify the table to suit the type of inversion you can do.
   - Choose from a shoulder stand, a partner-assisted handstand, a handstand at the wall, or a handstand on your own.
   - You may still be figuring out how to perform a handstand. Don't worry: this exercise will help you pinpoint how you can improve.

Choose a partner to work with Ask your partner to assess your technique and to tick 'Mastered', 'Nearly there' or 'Needs more practice'.

	Correct technique: shoulder stand			
Start position	Is the gymnast lying flat on their back on a mat?	○	○	○
	Are the knees bent and tucked in tight to the chest? Are the shoulders kept on the mat?	○	○	○
Balance	Are the hands placed under the hips, with the elbows on the mat? Are the elbows tucked in tight against the body?	○	○	○
	Does the gymnast lift the hips up over the shoulders, using the core and the hands?	○	○	○
	Do the hands move to the lower back for support? Are the elbows kept tight to the body, supporting some of the weight?	○	○	○
	Is all the weight now on the shoulders and the elbows?	○	○	○
	Is the gymnast comfortable now? Do they extend the legs straight upwards and point the toes towards the ceiling?	○	○	○
	Is the chin against the chest? Is the gymnast looking directly up at the feet?	○	○	○
Finish	Is the body in a straight line from the shoulders to the toes?	○	○	○
	Is the balance held still, with all weight on the shoulders and elbows?	○	○	○

Correct technique: handstand			
Are the hands shoulder-width apart?	○	○	○
Are the fingers spread wide for balance?	○	○	○
Are the elbows locked straight?	○	○	○
Are the shoulders shrugged and locked in place?	○	○	○
Is the head looking towards the hands?	○	○	○
Are the shoulders, hips, knees and ankles in line?	○	○	○
Are the legs squeezed together tightly?	○	○	○
Are the toes pointed?	○	○	○
Is the balance held still for 3 seconds?	○	○	○

2. With a partner, choose another inversion.

   • Design a technique checklist for this inversion, based on the tables on pp.258–259.

   • You can choose a bunny hop, cartwheel, headstand or any other inversion.

   • When you have completed the checklist with your partner, use it to assess each other's technique.

Correct technique:			
	○	○	○
	○	○	○
	○	○	○
	○	○	○
	○	○	○
	○	○	○

6. Balance 2

You have already learned that balance is when the body is held steady in a specific position. In this task, you will focus on partner balances: where two or three gymnasts work together to hold both bodies in position. This requires support, cooperation and a lot of focus on moving safely.

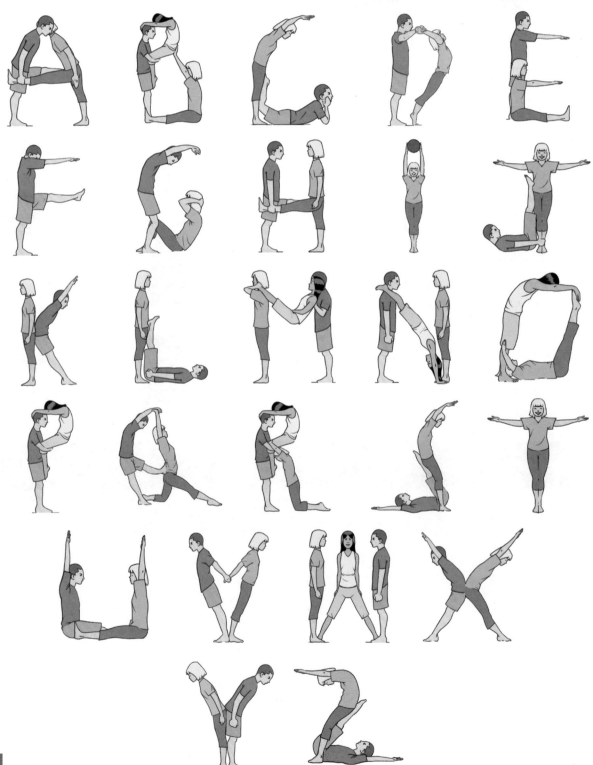

Task

Alphabet balances

1. Practise the alphabet balances (p.260) with your partners. Circle the ones can you do.

2. Choose one alphabet balance. Describe one way of getting into this balance, if it was part of a sequence. For example: *We could both teddy bear roll and finish in position to form the letter U.*

_____

_____

_____

_____

3. Work with your partners to spell out a word using the alphabet balances. Briefly describe how you could link the balances/letters to make a short sequence.

_____

_____

_____

_____

4. How many other symbols can you and your partners create using balances? Draw them here. Take time to practise and record them.

5. Choose one of the alphabet balances you cannot perform. Give one reason why you think you cannot do it. What would you need to change to be able to perform it?

_____

_____

_____

_____

7. Creativity

One of the best things about gymnastics is that it gives you the chance to be creative. You can use your imagination and your skills to design sequences. You can use themes and music to shape your creative performance.

Task

1. Design a short sequence of movement: on your own, with a partner, or in a group.

   Your sequence will contain:

   - Two forms of travel
   - Two jumps
   - Fast movements
   - Two rolls
   - Two balances
   - Slow movements

   Complete the following table to describe your sequence. Use the terms and movements you have learned in this chapter. Write the moves you will do in the appropriate column, depending on whether you do an individual, partner or group sequence.

Routine	Individual	Partner	Group
Travel			
Rolls			
Jumps			
Balances			
Fast movements			
Slow movements			

2. Practise and perform your sequence. Ask your partner to answer the questions below to assess your technique. Your partner will circle the most appropriate answer.

   - Are the movements controlled?   **All**   **Most**   **Some**   **None**
   - Does the gymnast use a lot of the space?   **All**   **Most**   **Some**   **None**
   - Do they use different levels?   **High**   **Medium**   **Low**
   - Do they use quick and slow movements?   **Lots**   **Some**   **No, only quick**   **No, only slow**

- How could they improve their control?

_____

_____

- How could they improve the overall aesthetics of the sequence?

_____

_____

3. This task focuses on your creative abilities.

   Work in a small group. Choose a theme. Design and perform a gymnastic sequence. Be as creative as possible, while also designing a sequence that showcases your ability.

   - Include examples of all the elements you have learned so far: locomotion, flight, rolling, inversion, balance, etc.

   - Record the sequence and give your evaluation below.

Who I worked with	
Theme	
How we decided what to include	
Three important factors in preparing for our sequence	• • •
Watching the recording of the sequence, I see these three things that could be improved	• • •
Watching the recording of the sequence, I see these three things that went well	• • •
I would change this aspect of the sequence	
I would change this aspect because	

4. Now that you have evaluated the sequence and your experience, work with your group to agree on any changes that can be made to improve the sequence. Perform your improved sequence for the class.

8. Warm-up

Before taking part in any sport, you need to prepare your body for the activity. Warm-ups will get your body ready for the activity, and will help you to avoid injury. In this section, we will look at the specifics of gymnastics warm-ups.

Task

1. Complete the table below. Describe one movement you can do as a warm-up for each of the body areas. Practise each warm-up. Think about how each body part feels before and after the warm-up.

Head/neck	
Shoulders	
Back	
Hips	
Knees	
Ankles	
Wrists	

2. Why is it important to warm up before physical activity?

_____

_____

3. Do you think this is important for gymnastics? Why?

_____

_____

_____

4. Do you think it is important for other activities? Which ones? Why?

_____

_____

5. Plan and design a warm-up suitable for a gymnastics class where students will be jumping, rolling, inverting and balancing.

- Ensure that all areas of the body are prepared for the class.

- The warm-up will be no more than 5 minutes.

- Describe your warm-up, using bullet points, pictures and key words. Alternatively, record yourself doing the warm up.

9. Balance 3

Group balances require communication, cooperation, strength and an awareness of how to move safely.

You have already learned that balances can be performed on many points of contact. An individual handstand involves two points of contact, since only your two hands touch the mat.

Task

1. Draw an appropriate balance in each of the spaces below. Include a mix of individual, partner and group balances. Practise these balances.

Balance with **four** points of contact	Balance with **four** points of contact

Balance with **three** points of contact	Balance with **three** points of contact

Balance with **two** points of contact	Balance with **two** points of contact

Balance with **one** point of contact	Balance with **one** point of contact

2. Below are some examples of group balances that require four or more people.
    Circle the ones you and your group can perform.

3. Work with your group to design a unique group balance that you can perform safely. Draw an outline of the balance below. Give a brief description of how to perform it.

4. What physical attributes help you to balance well?

5. Balance is vital in gymnastics and in other sports too. Name some other sports where it is useful to have good balance.

10. Sequencing

A gymnastics sequence is when two or more skills are performed, one after another. When a sequence is done correctly, the movements will flow: the ending of one movement will form the beginning of the next. There is no stopping or starting during the sequence. Showing continuous movement in your sequence is very important in gymnastics. Matching, mirroring, theme, symmetry and asymmetry are important in sequencing.

Matching	Showing a copy of the shape	☐
Mirroring	Showing a reflection of the shape	☐
Theme	An idea that runs through a piece of work; the central topic of a sequence	☐
Symmetry	A shape that is the same on both sides of the body; or a mirror image of a partner	☐
Asymmetry	A shape that is different on each side of the body; or different from a partner	☐

Task

1. Practise each of the terms above, with a partner. Tick all the ones you can complete.

2. Practise and describe how you could travel over the floor on your feet, showing changes in direction:

   • Forwards _____

   • Backwards _____

   • Sideways _____

3. Practise and describe how you could travel over the floor, using the following levels:

   • High _____

   • Medium _____

   • Low _____

4. Practise and describe how you could move on one part of your body, and then change to another body part. (Do not use the same body part twice.)

   • Change in level _____

   • Change in direction _____

   • Change in speed _____

5. Name some body parts on which you can easily hold your weight.

_____

_____

6. Practise and describe (or draw) how you could move slowly from one body part to another, then quickly from one body part to another.

_____

_____

7. Can you reverse the sequence?

_____

8. Draw the mirror of this shape. Then draw the match of this shape.

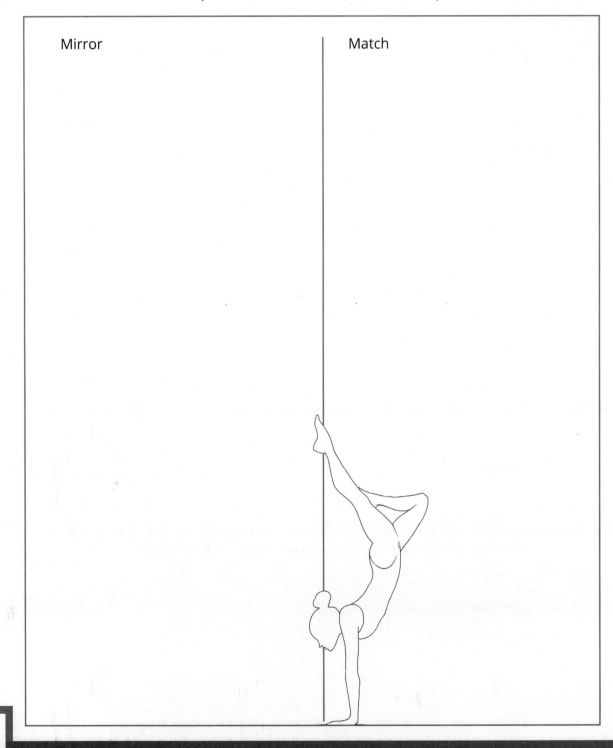

Mirror   Match

9. Practise and describe how you and a partner could perform some asymmetrical balances to produce one matching balance **and** one mirror balance.

_____

_____

_____

10. Can you add apparatus to your balance?

_____

11. Can you include how to travel to and from your balance with fluency?

_____

12. Work in a group of four. Design and record a sequence that shows change of level, direction and speed. Start and end your sequence with a paired match/mirror balance. Include:
    - Two symmetrical jumps

    - Two asymmetrical balances

    - Two different rolls.

13. Watch the recording of your sequence from Question 12.
    - Design a technique checklist for the sequence.

    - Base your checklist on what you have learned so far. Use headings from other checklists in this chapter.

    - Look back over this chapter and choose four key criteria points that you can use to self-evaluate your sequence.

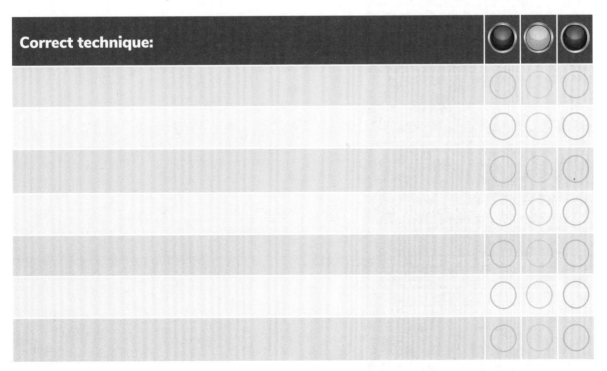

Correct technique:	⬤	⬤	⬤
	○	○	○
	○	○	○
	○	○	○
	○	○	○
	○	○	○
	○	○	○
	○	○	○

**End-of-unit assessment 1:
Group sequence**

Designing our sequence

- Design, describe and practise a group sequence.

- Ensure that your sequence contains all the elements in the table below.
  In the table, give a brief description for each element.

- Be creative with your sequence. Everyone needs to take part and showcase
  their abilities.

> **Note:** Not everyone needs to perform every single element, but
> every element should be included in your sequence. There are
> many options for each element. For example, if you have an
> excellent cartwheeler in your group, you may want to show off
> this skill – but not everybody in the group has to do a cartwheel!

Our sequence	
Element	**Description**
Theme	
Opening and closing group balance	
Change in levels	
• Two examples of flight • Two examples of rotation	
One example of inversion	
• One example of symmetry • One example of asymmetry	

Assessing our sequence

Record your performance and use the checklist below to assess your sequence.

Checklist: our sequence				
Quality	**Description**	⦿	◯	⦿
Efficient	We do not make unnecessary movements when we perform	◯	◯	◯
Pre-determined	We know what we are trying to achieve	◯	◯	◯
Coordinated	Everything is in time and is well linked	◯	◯	◯
Fluent	The skill is smooth, coordinated and flowing	◯	◯	◯
Aesthetic	The sequence looks good when we perform it	◯	◯	◯
Controlled	The movement is under control at all times	◯	◯	◯
Creative	We created a unique design and sequence of movements	◯	◯	◯

Reflecting on our sequence

Use the table below to write a brief reflection on your experience.

Designing a group sequence	Positives	
	Challenges	
Practising a group sequence	Positives	
	Challenges	
Performing a group sequence	Positives	
	Challenges	
Changes for next time		

End-of-unit assessment 2: Individual skill performance

Read through this classroom-based assessment in full before you begin.

My sportsperson's profile

Choose a famous sportsperson.
* Write a brief profile of the sportsperson, including the details below.

> **Note:** You do not need to choose a gymnast. If you can find footage of a sportsperson performing your chosen skill, you can profile that sportsperson. For example: you may be able to find footage of Serena Williams doing a flip, Conor McGregor doing a handstand, or a Premier League player doing a log roll!

Photo

* Date of birth:

* Birthplace:

* Lives:

* Club/team:

* Coach/manager:

* Career highlights:

* Profile:

My sportsperson's technique

Find footage of your profiled sportsperson performing a gymnastics skill. Create a short checklist to assess the technique of this sportsperson. Look back over this chapter to help you remember the technical points for this skill.

My sportsperson's gymnastics skill:	●	◐	●
Technical point			
	○	○	○
	○	○	○
	○	○	○
	○	○	○
	○	○	○
	○	○	○

My technique

Record yourself performing the same skill as the sportsperson. Use the same checklist from above to assess your technique performing the skill. Highlight one or two areas where you are as good as this sportsperson. Highlight one or two areas where you can improve to become as good as this sportsperson.

My gymnastics skill:	●	◐	●
Technical point			
	○	○	○
	○	○	○
	○	○	○
	○	○	○
	○	○	○
	○	○	○

My plan to improve

What areas do you need to work on to improve this skill: efficiency, coordination, fluency, control? Use the table below to identify some exercises that would help you to improve.

Needs improvement	Exercise to help

1. Design an activity that would help you to improve your technique. Use the information from the checklist on p.276 to help you focus on the key areas for development.

2. Why would you like to master this skill?

3. Where else could you use the skill?

4. You have studied a gymnastics skill in detail in this assessment. Evaluate yourself one last time to see if you have improved.

- Complete the checklist below.

- Base your new checklist on the checklist you designed on p.276.

- Highlight any areas where you have improved.

My gymnastics skill:			
Technical point			
	○	○	○
	○	○	○
	○	○	○
	○	○	○
	○	○	○
	○	○	○

Did you improve? In which areas? Why do you think this happened?

_____

_____

_____

_____

_____

_____

_____

_____

_____

_____

_____

_____

_____

_____

_____

_____

Strand review
In this chapter, you learned about:

- The importance of body control ☐
- A new vocabulary of skills specific to gymnastics ☐
- Physical literacy in gymnastics ☐
- Designing and performing a gymnastics sequence of movement ☐
- Evaluating a gymnastics sequence ☐

- Assessing your own and your partner's ability to perform a skill, using technical points ☐
- Working cooperatively with others to fulfil gymnastics tasks ☐
- Themes and building sequences based on themes ☐
- Critiquing and using feedback to improve an overall performance ☐

Look back over the activities you completed. Tick the skills you used.

Managing Myself	Staying Well	Managing Information and Thinking	Being Numerate
I know myself better ☐	I am healthy and active ☐	I gathered and analysed information ☐	I estimated, predicted and calculated ☐
I made decisions ☐	I am social ☐	I thought creatively ☐	I was interested in problem-solving ☐
I set goals ☐	I am safe ☐	I thought about what I learned ☐	
I achieved goals ☐	I feel confident ☐		
I thought about what I learned ☐	I feel positive about what I learned ☐	I used digital technology to access, manage and share information ☐	
I used technology to learn ☐			

Being Creative	Working with Others	Communicating	Being Literate
I thought about things from a different point of view ☐	I developed relationships ☐	I listened to my classmates ☐	I understood some new words ☐
I put ideas into action ☐	I dealt with conflict ☐	I expressed myself ☐	I wrote for different reasons ☐
I learned in a creative way ☐	I cooperated ☐	I performed/presented ☐	I expressed my ideas clearly ☐
I was creative with digital technology ☐	I respected difference ☐	I had a discussion/debate ☐	I developed my spoken language ☐
	I learned with others ☐	I used digital technology to communicate ☐	I read and wrote in different ways ☐
	I worked with others using digital technology ☐		

Discuss two skills (above) that you intend to focus on more in the future.

_____

_____

_____

_____

Apps for wellbeing

Chapter 09

Relaxation

Headspace

What it is: This is a mindfulness app designed to help us understand the mind and the world around us.

What it does: It teaches mindfulness and meditation, and aims to guide you towards living a healthier, happier life. Learning how to be mindful can be useful to you in all kinds of everyday situations. It can teach you to manage stress, think clearly and relate better to those around you.

Aura

What it is: This is a meditation app that focuses purely on relaxing the mind and body through the art of meditation.

What it does: It provides a new 3-minute guided meditation every day. Meditations vary according to your personal circumstances (e.g. age, health and interests) as well as current mood. Meditation helps with sleep, concentration, relaxation and managing anxiety.

Insight Timer

What it is: This is a mindfulness app that comes with a wealth of features and a variety of teachers.

What it does: It aids mindfulness and meditation. It gives you tips on how to minimise and manage stress. It provides lectures and podcasts on mindful topics. There are thousands of guided mediations with beautiful ambient sounds and gentle interval bells. This is the most popular free meditation app available today!

INSIGHT
Peace in our Timer

MyFitnessPal

What it is: This is a tracker for healthy diet and exercise. It gives more in-depth information than some other apps, when it comes to nutrition and physical activity.

What it does: It encourages you not to count calories, but to count nutrients. It shows you how to do this to make the most of your healthy diet. It has a relatively easy-to-use food and exercise diary. It tracks your intake of nutrients (carbohydrates, fats, protein and vitamins), fibre and water. It tracks your intake of sugar. It alerts you to nutritional areas that are being over- or under-consumed. It combines this data with your daily exercise count, and provides daily and weekly summaries on your progress.

Bonus: This app can be linked to other apps and fitness trackers so that you can record data.

Runkeeper

What it is: This is a GPS movement tracker app that lets you track your movement (walk, run or cycle). It helps you to set goals, stay motivated and monitor your progress.

What it does: It allows you to monitor distance, speed, time and heart rate in many different activities. You can set goals to work towards: the app will keep you motivated to achieve your targets! The app includes personal plans, challenges you can join, and virtual races you can take part in.

Bonus: This app works behind the scenes while you are listening to music. You can play music as normal and the app will not cause annoying interruptions! When you hit a milestone distance or time, the app will lower the volume of your music, give you the details and turn up the music again.

C25K

What it is: C25K stands for 'couch to 5 km'. There are several C25K apps. The 5K Trainer (Couch Potato to Running 5K) app by Zen Labs is free. It provides an easy, fun training plan for beginner runners.

What it does: It provides a programme designed for inexperienced runners who are just beginning an exercise routine. The structured plan helps to motivate beginner runners, using time challenges that keep moving forward with a mix of running and walking. This gradually helps you to build strength and stamina for a full 5 km run. The app is compatible with Spotify and many other music apps. It can also work with MyFitnessPal to log and to track your overall health.

Note: There are many C25K apps out there. This Zen Labs app is free and has lots of useful features. However, there are many C25K apps you can try!

Movement analysis

BaM Video Delay (iOS devices) or Video Coach (android)

What it is: These are video delay apps that allow quick video feedback by showing repeated footage.

What it does: These apps record you performing a skill in real time, and allow you to watch the footage on repeat. You can set the interval between each repeat. You can also set the number of repeats you will see. This app is useful for self-checking your technique and your general movement.

Hudl Technique

What it is: This app allows you to record and analyse movement technique. (The app was formerly known as Ubersense.)

What it does: It enables your smart device to record and break down movement technique for instant feedback. You can analyse skill performance using slow motion and drawing tools. You can also trim and edit videos to isolate the technical points you are assessing. You can import video footage from your library, compare against a previous performance, and even compare your performance to that of a professional sportsperson!

Video Tagger

What it is: This is a video analysis and assessment tool that allows you to capture and tag sports performance. You can do this during your class to produce highlight videos.

What it does: It enables you to record footage and simultaneously tag what you see taking place. The tags are customised to suit the performance you want to observe. For example: while recording a game of badminton, you could set one tag on the smash. When you have finished recording, every smash during the game will be compiled into one video.

- Many sportswear companies have produced useful apps, including Fitbit, Nike, Garmin, Samsung and Under Armour.

- You might also like to try some sleep tracker apps, including Sleep Cycle and SleepBot.

My apps

Technology changes so rapidly that many of the apps we know today can be out of date by tomorrow! Use this page to list any other apps that you like, that you think are better, or that your classmates recommend.

App name:

What it is:

What it does:

_____
_____

App name:

What it is:

What it does:

_____
_____

App name:

What it is:

What it does:

_____
_____

App name:

What it is:

What it does:

_____
_____

Reflective Journal

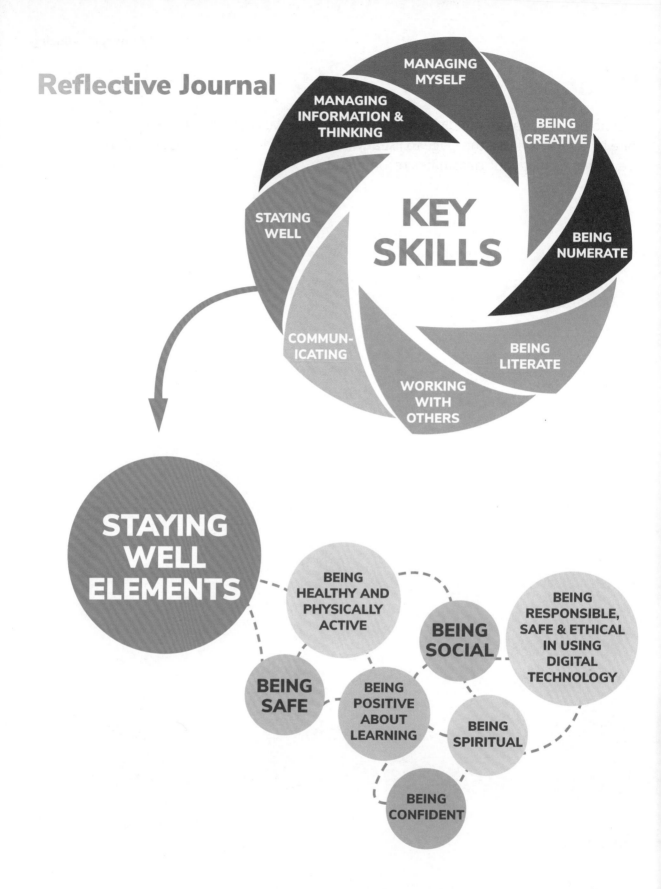

Each of these balls represents one element of Staying Well, which is a Key Skill of the Junior Cycle programme. It is important to experience as many of these elements as possible during your time in school. The reflection boxes in this chapter will help you to think about some of the experiences you have had in PE and will assist you in exploring what these experiences meant to you.

Reflective Journal

Module title:

Staying Well Element 1

Describe the scenario.

_____

How did this impact on me?

_____

How can I apply this beyond PE class?

_____

Staying Well Element 2

Describe the scenario.

_____

How did this impact on me?

_____

How can I apply this beyond PE class?

_____

Module title:

Staying Well Element 1

Describe the scenario.

_____

How did this impact on me?

_____

How can I apply this beyond PE class?

_____

Staying Well Element 2

Describe the scenario.

_____

How did this impact on me?

_____

How can I apply this beyond PE class?

_____

Reflective Journal

Module title:

Staying Well Element 1

Describe the scenario.

_____

How did this impact on me?

_____

How can I apply this beyond PE class?

_____

Staying Well Element 2

Describe the scenario.

_____

How did this impact on me?

_____

How can I apply this beyond PE class?

_____

Module title:

Staying Well Element 1

Describe the scenario.

_____

How did this impact on me?

_____

How can I apply this beyond PE class?

_____

Staying Well Element 2

Describe the scenario.

_____

How did this impact on me?

_____

How can I apply this beyond PE class?

_____

Reflective Journal

Module title:

Staying Well Element 1

Describe the scenario.

_____

How did this impact on me?

_____

How can I apply this beyond PE class?

_____

Staying Well Element 2

Describe the scenario.

_____

How did this impact on me?

_____

How can I apply this beyond PE class?

_____

Module title:

Staying Well Element 1

Describe the scenario.

_____

How did this impact on me?

_____

How can I apply this beyond PE class?

_____

Staying Well Element 2

Describe the scenario.

_____

How did this impact on me?

_____

How can I apply this beyond PE class?

_____

Reflective Journal

287

Reflective Journal

Module title:

Staying Well Element 1

Describe the scenario.

_____

How did this impact on me?

_____

How can I apply this beyond PE class?

_____

Staying Well Element 2

Describe the scenario.

_____

How did this impact on me?

_____

How can I apply this beyond PE class?

_____

Module title:

Staying Well Element 1

Describe the scenario.

_____

How did this impact on me?

_____

How can I apply this beyond PE class?

_____

Staying Well Element 2

Describe the scenario.

_____

How did this impact on me?

_____

How can I apply this beyond PE class?

_____

Reflective Journal

Module title:

Staying Well Element 1
Describe the scenario.

How did this impact on me?

How can I apply this beyond PE class?

Staying Well Element 2
Describe the scenario.

How did this impact on me?

How can I apply this beyond PE class?

Module title:

Staying Well Element 1
Describe the scenario.

How did this impact on me?

How can I apply this beyond PE class?

Staying Well Element 2
Describe the scenario.

How did this impact on me?

How can I apply this beyond PE class?

Reflective Journal

Module title:

Staying Well Element 1

Describe the scenario.

_____

How did this impact on me?

_____

How can I apply this beyond PE class?

_____

Staying Well Element 2

Describe the scenario.

_____

How did this impact on me?

_____

How can I apply this beyond PE class?

_____

Module title:

Staying Well Element 1

Describe the scenario.

_____

How did this impact on me?

_____

How can I apply this beyond PE class?

_____

Staying Well Element 2

Describe the scenario.

_____

How did this impact on me?

_____

How can I apply this beyond PE class?

_____